C000228394

A HUMOUR OF LOVE

A HUMOUR OF LOVE

A MEMOIR

ROBERT MONTAGU

QUARTET

First published in 2014 by Quartet Books Limited
A member of the Namara Group
27 Goodge Street, London W1T 2LD
Copyright © Robert Montagu 2014
The right of Robert Montagu to be identified
as the author of this work has been asserted
by him in accordance with the
Copyright, Designs and Patents Act, 1988
All rights reserved.
No part of this book may be reproduced in
any form or by any means without prior
written permission from the publisher
A catalogue record for this book
is available from the British Library
ISBN 978 0 7043 7366 2
Typeset by Josh Bryson
Printed and bound in Great Britain by
T J International Ltd, Padstow, Cornwall

Dedicated to my wife Marzia,
without whom I would not have found the way back

This book would not have been published without the good-will of my wife and children, my agent Margaret Hanbury and Naim Attallah from Quartet

If you would like to support my work with children who have been emotionally disturbed, please contribute to the funds of the Dorset Child and Family Counselling Trust, which you can find on the website www.dcfct.org

'He was to imagine me his love, his mistress;
And I set him every day to woo me.
At which time would I, being but a moonish youth,
Grieve, be effeminate, changeable, longing and liking,
Proud, fantastical, apish, shallow, inconstant,
Full of tears, full of smiles;
For every passion something, and for no passion truly anything,
As boys and women are for the most part
Cattle of this colour –
Would now like him, now loathe him;
Then entertain him, then forswear him,
Now weep for him, then spit at him,
That I drave my suitor from his mad humour of love
To a living humour of madness…'

Act 3, Scene 2, *As You Like It*
William Shakespeare

'All that is necessary for the triumph of evil is
that good men do nothing.'
Edmund Burke

PROLOGUE

It's grand fun writing a prologue, isn't it? My English teacher would be pleased to see me do it. He would be less pleased to see WHERE – on an old cane chair with bits of bamboo seat missing, in a lugubrious ruined castle outside Rome, trying to make sense of life at the age of sixteen. It's 1966 and young people seem to be in charge of everything. You can almost see the granddads curling up their toes and turning to the wall not to hear the raucous music blasting from the speakers and threatening their way of life. Long-haired hippies who never went through a war! Get lost, the lot of you.

I'm starting out in adult life, having run away from school a month ago for good or evil. My mother would say *for evil* as I am entering the world without qualifications or prospects. She would say – trying to buck up my ideas – that I will be good only to wash lavatories in a public convenience. My plan is that I will find my way forward but only when I have made some sense of the past. You have to get the reverse gear sorted out before venturing to move forward. I have to clear up a whole mess of things that happened to me when I was younger and make sense of this humour of love business with my father. If I cannot do that, there can be no forward gear. I may as well do what I thought of often when I was eleven and find a way to finish things. That wouldn't be so bad. There's always a grand new beginning somewhere in a different world, if you take the view of an optimist.

I'm with this mad Anglican monk at the moment. His name is Father Perceval and we've been together off and on during the last few months, in the sense that we saw each other often at school during the summer. Father P didn't have his post renewed in the autumn whereas I did a bunk in late September; two guys thrown off the education roller-coaster, though in the padre's case the contract was always going to be temporary. The deal is we're here in this ruined castle for a wintry month because my dear mother thought it would be a grand idea for two old cronies to get together to plan the next stages of our lives, with so much to share about our feelings. The alternative was for me to kick up my heels in London over the winter, getting over jaundice and looking wan and morose, as if NEXT SECOND I would be taking cannabis and LSD with other similar roller-coaster casualties.

We're borrowing this ruined castle free of charge from a wealthy owner with plenty of other properties to occupy. He has only asked that we keep the place clean and apply the odd lick of paint if we feel so inclined. We have a month's stay until mid-November when I go back to a glorious seventeenth birthday among my adoring clan – I don't think. Some sister will instead be telling me what a hideous future life has in store for me without A-levels. Father Perceval will be returning to a Franciscan base at Oxford to await his next assignment.

I'm going to be spending my time unravelling the dreadful business of my past by writing it down step by step and in deepest secret. If the padre finds out what I am doing – let alone anyone else – he'll want to share in my story syllable by syllable and, being who he is, will desire to comment and bathe in the luxury of it like a bubble bath. I might just scream the place down while he does. My story will come out in haphazard form because that's the way it is inside my head. It will also be full of questions and imaginary answers because I am in dire need of both, never having been given explanations for what happened. The narrative will no doubt show I am as culpable as anyone else. I will be aiming the questions chiefly at my father and mother and myself; they're the prime witnesses to my disasters. So if I use the word *YOU*, it will tend to mean one or other of them; *I* will obviously be me. The answers will be imagined unless I quote them in italics, in which case they have been *spoken and recorded in my brain*.

As to whether my parents will ever read this missal, I am none too sure of that. Probably it is a document I will throw away as soon as I have written it; otherwise I will hold onto it in a secret drawer. What could possibly happen is that I will publish the damn thing one day and be done with it. In case the MS falls into the wrong hands – for example, Father Perceval's – I am going to disguise most of the characters by giving them different names; the same with places. Some people will say this is a fudge and a cowardly approach to an important matter. I say it is necessary to protect the innocent as well as the *wicked*; the wicked always need extra protection. I am not so much concerned with naming and punishment anyway. I am writing chiefly to sort out the mess inside my head…and to see if I can record what can happen when a small boy and his father get tangled up notions about love.

PART ONE

I have vague memories aged four or five of sitting on a huge lawn eating a picnic under the shadow of a cedar tree. My mother is passing out the plates and food efficiently with the help of a nanny and a housekeeper. Dad is wearing a tweed suit with a mustard-coloured jersey and a tie, grinning as if he's on parade, which perhaps he is and we are too…surrounded by gardeners, house servants and gawping visitors. Normally they see Dad in an elegant drawing room or sitting behind a desk scribbling notes for staff, unless they have gone to the visitors' gallery of the House of Commons where they might find him with his hands holding his lapels, haranguing his own Conservative government. The older children are spread out across a vast rug. There are a bewildering number. Let's start from the eldest and work down: two teenage girls, one with frizzy blonde hair and a narrow jaw while the other has wider bone structure and dark, longer hair, looking a bit like my mother; next comes my older brother with a rounder face and straight, straw-coloured hair; he is about twelve; then comes another pair of sisters - one prettier than the other with a slimmer shape and thick shoulder length hair and the other with wavy locks and a rounded jaw. She has a constant laugh and is aged around seven.

I'm the youngest of the family, in the middle. You might call me the piggy but I am passed round like the prince.

This formal picnic happens none too often. My Dad is busily immersed in politics, fighting unlikely causes and forming pressure groups of one sort or another: for example, he is violently anti-common market. My mother is busy attending parties or painting in her London studio and visiting other artists. My brother and sisters have fun playing in the woods and lake areas, raiding islands and pretending to be pirates, while I am still being guarded by a hairy-lipped nanny who feeds me food specially mashed and sieved. My sisters are jealous about that as they detested their strict governess and managed to get rid of her by smashing and sprinkling her spectacles down a drainpipe. Occasionally my sisters make me pay for my privileged position by calling wolf noises through a ventilation pipe in my room. The sound whirls round my head and I spring up with cries of terror, thinking I am about to be devoured.

A lot of my time seems to be spent in bed: the family belief being that the youngest needs most rest. I could argue with that. It means I miss out on what is happening between my parents. I am paraded in front of them by my nanny only during tea when guests may take me on their knee for petting purposes. By the time I am five, my parents are already splitting up and going their separate ways. The vision I have of all of us sitting at that formal picnic is one of the only times when we are together ever.

Around this time I wake on a calm night with the full moon shining and walk to the window to look out.

I realise it is not far down to the ground. I have been practising jumping from the branches of the cedar tree onto the main lawn. I think I can jump down from this narrow window ledge. I climb out and rest my bottom on the sill. The ground seems close in the moonlight. Shall I jump down or return to bed and prove what a ninny I am with more wailing at the wolves?

Next morning I tell the family at breakfast the story of my heroic leap. They are gathered on two sides of the long Cromwellian refectory table. There is a ritual in passing the jam; you have to ask if the next person has finished with it and then wait for an eternity while it is passed from hand to hand.

'You JUMPED?' my brother repeats with a hoot of disbelief. 'Don't be silly, Robert. It must be at least twelve feet from the nunnery window to the ground.'

'I DID jump,' I insist.

'You did not,' says Kate. 'Don't tell a fib.'

My father is laughing gently and looking proud of my claim. There is a buttonhole in his lapel: a sweet-smelling jasmine that he has picked personally from the conservatory, ready to defy the Opposition benches.

'Hush, everyone. Let the boy speak. If Robert says he jumped from the nursery window, then he did,' he says.

My mother looks crossly at my father. His romantic idealism will be the death of us, maybe she's thinking.

'Then how did the boy get back inside the house?' she asks. 'When all the doors are locked? How come he didn't hurt his ankles and feet on the cobbles in the courtyard? Don't encourage him,' she says. 'Or Robbie

will get ideas and next time the boy may smash his head.'

Am I being a fantasist or did I really jump? It is not the first or last time I have been forced to re-examine my story as you shall see. Of course I did, I tell myself. I remember how important it was for me not to prove myself a ninny. Surely I remember falling through the air.

There are probably a good many reasons why my father and mother decided to abandon each other when I was five but none have so far been given to me. So I shall improvise and guess. Some guesses will be more obvious than others. Some will be so personal that electricity will be passed through my body even for recording such ideas. However they are what a sixteen year old comes up with when he feels nothing has ever been explained. They are the dregs of an angry imagination.

One: *YOU* – Dad – were so busy running importantly up and down to Parliament in your Bentley that family needs were the last thing on your mind. It was no longer convenient travelling two hours north to a vast country house that was castellated like a palace. You had your father living next door in a humdrum cottage and secretly you loathed his guts. The biggest pull was your exciting political life: the intrigues and social change going on in London. You were wholly committed to that life. You even wrote and published a pamphlet on the future society you wanted for Britain, as if you and your cronies might easily take over one day in some form of coup d'état. You took dinner at your various clubs surrounded by admirers and attended constant cocktails and personal soirees. Why go home to children who were running screaming down draughty corridors and making wolf noises at night? Why go home to a wife with different needs from yours and her own personal agenda? You had lived the life of marriage and babies for more than twenty years by the time I was five. It was time to grow beyond being a Dad.

TWO: Mum and you belonged in different places on the political spectrum. She had supported you by sitting alongside during endless speeches. She had even led women's parades in support of your opinions up and down the streets. However in private your views were often poles apart, wider than Mao Tse Tung and Genghis Khan. You were a Conservative of the old-fashioned kind that takes a riding crop to trade unionists; in fact, you would ship them off to the old British colonies if you had your way. My mother was an ardent liberal with friends on the Commons benches. She was a strong feminist, who once – before the war – outraged convention by walking into the Royal Yacht Squadron at Cowes dressed in trousers. How do you sit down comfortably together at a Party dinner with a wife like that, who might suddenly betray you with a remark that might have come from the mouth of the liberal leader?

THREE: When I was five, you were thinking of selling the family home. It was too large and expensive to run and needed a new roof. It was the ideal time to wave goodbye to my mother. 'You go off to London, darling, and do your artistic thing. Leave me to my politics.' My mother needed a home in London to house us. You reckoned you could settle on her some money from a sale. She could buy her own sanctuary. The children would then have two houses and two lifestyles to enjoy. What could be more logical than that?

I think you genuinely imagined we would be happier without a background of political and domestic bickering. What you didn't count on and regretted later was the break-up of your emotional bonds. Ties which are tiresome in proximity can chafe when they are broken. Restrictions that hold you back from foolishness in a marriage become essential when you are released. Certainly I didn't know the difference when I first went to London and came back as a child to Dorset. I sure as hell know now with more experience. It took two years to begin to discover how different the world could be without a combination of both parents.

FOUR: we're into more personal territory now. Never mind: the words need revealing and the thoughts need developing when I am struggling to comprehend. I have a right to record my guesses, however difficult they might be for everyone concerned. You two were beginning to part ways *erotically*, isn't that so? I say beginning but that doesn't do justice to the full extent. You had alternative visions of romance from the very start; I see that now.

You, Dad, were probably given a sexual education by your own father. There now – I've said THAT. I may be wrong and I am certainly guessing without 100% knowledge but it makes good sense. I believe that George taught all his children about sex – or tried to do so. Your younger brother may have escaped but your sisters didn't and neither did you, I guess. Later on you developed gay interests during your school days. You maintained a personal following among men and boys after you were married. Oh, yes, I am beginning to see that now! I am beginning to put the pieces of the puzzle together. You probably had special friends among your political and social milieu that had greater interests at a bachelor party than – shall we say – comparing ways to dry a handkerchief. I dare say I will find out more details in years to come, if I am that interested. All I would need to do is search out old cronies of yours and invite them to a private soiree. I am sure I would know the truth even from their faces: which ones go a tomato red when asked about your boyfriends.

You too, Mum, had a thing about your gender ever since you were a girl. I know that because of what happened later on. Also I heard not long ago from a sister that the year you were engaged to Dad, you attended a ball in the south of France. Your father caught you looking with vivid interest at a girl who was dancing, instead of at her male partner. He tut-tutted and told you that you should be looking the other way. I'm also told another fact: that at the time I was ringing the bell inside your womb trying to get out, you were busy hanging curtains in a girlfriend's flat. So there, detective Robert is on your case as well, *Mamma!* Don't think I am not.

Sure, I am vexed by the question, *why did you each leave the other?* If you hadn't, things would have turned out vastly differently for me. After all, I took your place with Dad, didn't I, *Mamma?* That's the truth from which we can none of us hide. I took your place and performed your duties. If you had remained a constant in Dad's life, I wouldn't have been cast in the role of substitute. Many times after the spilt – when we were together in bed – Dad would remind me when he had finished how much he loved and was missing YOU.

Father Perceval was nosing around this morning, setting off late to go to Rome where he is doing some ecumenical business. He has taken a temporary job in an orphanage for boys. He is going to be assisting in some welfare reforms along the lines he brought into Eton College while I was there. He is also holding talks with people at the Vatican about supporting the financial arrangements of the English Franciscans, who are living in cramped accommodation. There is the vexed question of balancing income and expenditure and Father P has been loaned a small office to work on facts and figures.

Today the padre wanted to know what I had been doing for the first three days since we had arrived. How was it that no walls had yet been washed or even cleared of cobwebs? He thinks I am the convenient skivvy who is going to do all the housework while he swans around the eternal city spreading holy messages. He asked me if I thought this was the right way to proceed, by doing nothing while he slaved to earn a crust of bread. I opened my mouth to remind him it is my mother who has paid for most of our expenses. She has done so in the mistaken belief that it will help us to make the most of our time together and prevent him from worrying about money. Wrong, mother. The reality is that for the last three days Father P could not wait to get away from me. The reason is that he tried to jump on me the first night we got here. *Yes, sexually, he did.* He stopped me coming out of the bathroom when we went upstairs and tried to lure me along the corridor to his bedroom. 'Come along, dear boy. Come to Papa and warm my cockles.' He thought he had earned the right to take me there by offering his friendship during our time at school; not only by that but offering the stay in Rome. When I told him to get lost, he stomped off and headed for the eternal city in a fury next morning as soon as it got light. Whoops, Mum! That wasn't what you intended during this stay, was it? I don't think so. For me it came as something of a shock, I have to admit. I looked up to the man mightily. But there it was: another adult to add to the puzzles about love and lust.

Today the padre went off in a more mellow mood, leaving me sitting on my uncomfortable cane chair in front of a table that appeared to have been used at some time for chopping meat. I watched him out of the window rolling down the hillside as the man is on the plump side and his gown descends almost to the ground, exposing bare ankles and leather sandals. He was wearing a round black hat that he has found in some back street shop in Rome, complete with a loop that fits under the chin. It makes him look like Father Brown in a story by G.K.Chesterton.

Here I was sitting and thinking how I would spend the rest of my day. Perhaps I should be searching for a fine safe hiding place to stow my manuscript? Not under my mattress, that was certain, in case Father P came hunting for me again in the night.

It becomes a custom soon after I arrive in my father's magnificent house near Beaminster for me to run down the red-carpeted corridor to his bedroom in the early morning. I am six by that time and it's 1955. My father sleeps on the north side of the house and my room is on the south side above the kitchen. My sisters (the younger two) are in the attic above him while my brother occupies a four poster bed next door to me. I find my Dad already awake listening to an extended news programme on Radio 4. Some deep-voiced presenter is rabbiting on about politics: who said what to whom during which debate in Parliament. My father makes an occasional Hrumph or mutters under his breath about the presenter's ignorance of detail. He greets me warmly and instructs me to close the door.

We read nursery stories from a collection of books he has waiting on the shelf of his bedside table. Otherwise he will lie back with me beside him on the pillow. He tells me a story of his own invention or else gives his own rendition of a famous tale like Red Riding Hood or The Three Bears. I love the reworked tales the best because he changes his voice to suit the characters: taking on the deep voice of the father in The Three Bears or the kiddie voice of the child who hides behind the curtain and fails to conceal her small green slippers.

For the next year, this is all that happens. The housekeeper raps on the door at eight o'clock and enters bearing a large tray which she sets down on the bed. It has freshly squeezed orange juice for two and a pretty Chinese cup and saucer with a rice pattern beside a matching teapot. Dad fills the cup with Lapsang Souchong while Josie draws the curtains. I watch in fascination as the flowery tea leaves swirl round the cup. Someone has told me you can tell the future according to how the tea leaves settle. Dad takes a lump of white sugar from the silver bowl and dips it in the tea before bringing it to my mouth and popping it inside like a sweetie for a favourite seal.

'There you are, boyzo. Does that taste good?'

'Ummm.' I feel a little like a circus act. I should flip the sugar lump up in the air.

'Fine day, your Lordship,' says the cheerful house-keeper. 'Are you planning a picnic, Cook would like to know? Given the sun is shining today and there are hardly any clouds. That might be a good idea.'

Good idea for the staff as it means several hours off duty.

'Yes, I think we will,' says Dad, leaning over to glance at the sky through the leaded window pane. 'It's all blue up there.' He turns back to me. 'What do you think, Robbie? Wouldn't a picnic be fun? We can go down to the woods past Home Farm with the stream and the beech trees or else up into the fir trees past Hooke.'

I mumble my agreement. I love picnics, even if they are only half attended by the family; if my brother is on holiday with a French family it cannot be helped and my older sisters are staying with my mother in the Isle of Wight. I still have two other sisters present and maybe friends of my Dad's who are staying for the weekend.

The housekeeper goes out and closes the door. In the early days, I finish the orange juice and go off to dress so I can sniff around the kitchen before breakfast, hoping to be thrown a slice of raw pastry during the making of pies. I can spend hours in the kitchen nibbling while I stroke the housekeeper's cat, watching the cook's activity and chatting to her little girl. I might also nip out to the stables to feed the horses with an apple and run upstairs to the long room above where my father and I have laid out a double O gauge train track with complex points and handmade passenger trains.

By the time I am seven, the morning visit to my father takes a different form. Soon after the housekeeper leaves, he leans forward to kiss my brow as I am still munching noisily on the sugar lump.

'I do love you, boy,' he murmurs in my ear. 'So very much it hurts! Don't you love me?'

'Yes, I do,' I mumble.

I have clear evidence of this close affection. My father, who has the reputation of being a stern man, catches me to him often and kisses my cheek, my neck, my bare arms while we are walking or sitting on the sofa. Often my sisters are watching while he does this and I hear them twitch and mutter comments. Isn't it unfair the way their little brother receives so much attention? When were they last kissed by Dad so passionately? If my older brother is there, he may snort and turn away pretending he hasn't noticed.

'I do love you, Robs. You remind me so much of your mother,' Dad murmurs. He gestures to the door. 'Get up and lock the door, will you, darling? We don't want anyone else coming in to disturb our rest.'

I would welcome my sisters to come and jump on the bed any time they liked but of course they never do; they're fast asleep and probably snoring like billy-o. Also they have become self-conscious by the age of nine and twelve. They are beginning to grow boobies. Occasionally I see them coming and going from the bathroom in the Isle of Wight, hugging dressing gowns close to their bodies. Girls are funny that way, going shy in front of their families. Whereas I…well, I'm still happy to run down a corridor in the nude. Why shouldn't I? There's not much to hide.

I get up obediently and lock the door with the big brass key, leaving it inside the lock. Then I hop back into bed and snuggle up to my father's big body in his creamy silk pyjamas. Everything about him is large and hot. I like the big veined hands, the wide chest and dignified face which makes funny expressions when he is reading stories. I don't feel afraid; however I'm a touch cautious. I have seen him cross at times with other people; never me. I shouldn't like it to be my turn EVER.

'Aren't you hot?' Dad asks after a few moments. 'Wouldn't you like to take off your pyjama top, Robbie? That way you'll feel more comfortable.'

'I'm OK,' I shrug, feeling perfectly cool.

'No, take it off,' Dad orders with a trace of command. 'You look hot and we don't want you sweating.'

When have I ever sweated in bed? I'm as cool as the inside of a cucumber. But I shrug off the sleeves and my father helps, taking the jacket from me and throwing it across the chaise longue at the foot of the bed. He runs his hands over my chest as I lie back on the pillow. I wonder if he is going to resume the morning story and whether I should remind him. But why shouldn't he delay and stroke me? I am proud of the way my body is developing and my arms are covered in fine golden hairs.

'What about your pyjama bottoms?' Dad asks, pinching at the cotton. 'Shouldn't these come off as well? If you get hot, you'll need a bath before you dress.'

It's on my mind to ask why I should be naked. However I detect the faint note of resolution in my father's voice. If I refuse to follow his request, he could become irritated in the same way as he does with the servants or my sisters. He might sulk and brood all through the day.

He watches as I throw back the bedclothes and peel down my pyjama trousers. He helps to slide the material down my thighs. I have a slinky little frame with nothing special on display: a pencil-sized penis and balls the size of peanuts, a bottom that is like two halves of an unripe grape.

'That's better, boyzo,' Dad says in satisfaction. 'That's so much better.'

I draw the sheet over me to cover up but Dad likes to keep it low so he can look me over like some Carrara marble he has just bought in an antique shop. He seems to be breathing in the air from a forgotten world and I *wonder if it is me he is thinking of or some Narcissus in a fairy tale. Could it be himself when he was my age that he is thinking of?*

'Perfect,' he mutters. 'Glorious.'

His hands start to move across my body as if he is casting spells. Soon after that his head starts on a journey of discovery. His mouth starts pecking at my body with little kisses until he covers every inch of skin. I begin to understand why he has asked me to lock the door as the housekeeper or the girls would find this close attention most peculiar. They would have questions in their minds such as what it does for a man to nibble at his boy in this way: to kiss everything in sight and to suck.

So my first question for Dad is, *what happened to the morning story?* It seems the tale was set aside in the rush of interest over my body. But what can a boy my age offer his father that competes with a good nursery tale? It's a conundrum that has never been answered. If I was bold enough aged seven, I might have asked. It's the sort of question that requires an answer at some time whether or not it makes any sense.

Without Dad here, I shall have to have a go myself. I shall represent Dad's thoughts and feelings and see if I can find some sense in what they offer. I've had some time to think about this issue and get rid of the silliest rubbish. I'd say the reasons left over make some sense.

ONE: I was lonely, boyzo. It may be hard for you to understand, surrounded by your loving sisters and family and seeing me with friends up for the weekend, but it is so. Often I was busy entertaining and the time was spent with other adults. But you were my secret treasure. I was missing your mother desperately and you helped to fill in the gaps with something of her voice, of her smell and charm. You moved in similar ways and showed tenderness and love. Your hips were almost the same shape in miniature. When I was kissing your body, I could be with Rosie in my mind.

TWO: The interest in your body happened just the same with my Dad. George was often lonely in the bedroom department. He was no longer intimate with my mother after a time. Papa made up for her lack of intimacy by turning to his children for comfort. My younger brother escaped because he was cheeky and disobedient and knew how to say boo to a goose. I was more obliging. The exchange went on at school when I was older. There were boys interested in me and vica versa. Some of them I liked enormously and so I went with them willingly. That's the way it went. It was almost expected that some people shared a bed. Older boys would often care for juniors in that way. I went on from that to college and later into army training: always the same interests were present and somehow taken for granted. The habit stayed. It's still with me now and I'm not ashamed. The practice of pederasty was good enough for the ancient Greeks and Romans so why shouldn't it be good enough for me?

THREE: OK, so there's a power element in this. I'm a successful politician, landowner and aristocrat. I believe in power and its use in society. I'm a follower of Nietsche. Men who hold power earn the right to wield it. They have special dispensation from heaven as well as from their fellow men. Such special citizens require relaxation, love, attention and constant admiration. They have earned the honour to be indulged like generals after a successful war. Politicians are like peacocks: they are fond of sporting their colours. Why shouldn't they be allowed to preen in private? If I choose to kiss and cuddle my young son, then he should be pleased to be found worthy of such attention. I might be planting a medal on his chest when I cover it with kisses.

So I'm allowed to comment now, am I, Dad? – from my seven year old position. I'm allowed to tell you what this attention made me feel, if only inside my head? OK, thanks Dad.

ONE: I was honoured, yes. Wow! I was thinking: this is a bit odd but pretty special. Am I so important to him? Does my Dad do this with anyone else but me? Not as far as I know. There's only me here: certainly at eight o'clock in the morning. I have attracted an intense degree of attention. Is it love or should I call it something else? It makes me feel special, certainly. I have something in my life that is outside the ordinary. I don't see many boys of seven being cuddled in this way: not that I would know exactly. There are one or two examples outside the school gates in London but mostly they are little girls being picked up and cuddled. So yes, I'm honoured. What Dad is showing me is that I'm valuable. That gives me a warm glow.

TWO: Isn't this treatment peculiar, though? I mean the extent of the kissing and the stroking which can go on forever. Is this what adults do in bed when they are together? Is it right for me to be involved in this activity? Should I respond in some way helpfully? I know my Dad is thinking of my Mum. Can he see her in his mind's eye? But then why does he stare at my body so closely and some-times glance up at my face to check his activity is OK? He wants my approval of his actions. Should I speak or continue to make-believe that I'm asleep? But that means I am acting oddly as well as he is. We are in this thing together.

Father Perceval stared at me across the table this morning and asked what was on my mind. I said, nothing. He asked why it was that I wasn't speak-ing to him much when I came down this morning. Was I still angry about the first night? I said no - but what was there to talk about? He shrugged his shoulders. Then he asked when he could expect me to start on the household jobs we had promised round the castle. That HE had promised on MY be-half, I wanted to say but actually said nothing. So again he asked, what was on my mind? Was I still cross about the request to share a bed? I said that actually that HAD come as something of a shock.

I hadn't been expecting the invitation. He said he had thought what he wanted was obvious at school. Hadn't that come across? NO! I said a little forcefully. Not to me and not I hope to anyone else. Did we all seem to invite THAT? Father P said he was sorry for the misunderstanding. He had thought our talks together at Eton had laid the foundations for a later close friendship. BUT NOT LIKE THAT! I answered. After which we both went quiet.

This evening Father Perceval told me about his day in Rome. He had met a group of teenage boys at the orphanage who had formed a pop group. They wanted to perform at various venues so he had taken them on a tour of places looking for a gig. They found a café on the Via Nazionale that was prepared to give the group a trial. The audition was going to be in a few days' time. He asked if I would like to come along and watch. I shrugged and told him I would think about it.

I said I had made a start preparing the big room upstairs for paint. We went upstairs to take a look. I hadn't got far with the dusting, he pointed out, missing some cobwebs in the corners. I explained it was impossible to reach up there without a ladder. The heights of the ceilings must have been designed with giants in mind. Father P immediately walked over to the caretaker's cottage across the castle courtyard and returned with a stepladder so I could extend my reach.

We ate lamb chops he had brought back from Rome, washed down with some hearty swallows of wine. We sat round a log fire in the bare-floored sitting room, reading books until it was time to go to bed. I couldn't wait to sleep as I was exhausted but first I added this piece to my writing so as not to leave it for another day.

There's a black and white photo of me at the age of ten or eleven which sits on the corner of my father's desk, showing me in my Prep school uniform. I look somewhat like my Mum with soft hair and creamy skin and a mock alert expression on my face, as though butter wouldn't melt in my mouth but I'm sure as hell ready for anything. Dad had it taken by a photographer in London. I can imagine him eyeing the photo at this moment as he works away at his papers, wiping the tears from his eyes whenever he glances at the frame.

Mum is perhaps less moved by my absence from her house; it's hard to tell. I know she cries when she leaves me at the school gates for the first time because I can see the tears starting to her eyes as she drives away, with me chasing after the car as if determined to get lost in the exhaust.

'Gosh, was that your mother?' asks a new boy named Andrew, picking himself up from the gutter as his Mum has also just disappeared up the drive. 'I liked the black fur at her collar. She looks like a film actress.'

Andrew shows me something he thinks is interesting: the missing digit of a finger, chopped off with a hatchet by accident. This creates one friendship which is confirmed by sharing the same dormitory. As far as I am concerned, most of the boys in my year and the one above are bullies. They seem to delight in spending their lives making us apple pie beds and flicking towels at our privates.

I quickly discover the only way to avoid torment is by joining the choir. I do this by accident within the first term at school, by attempting to learn the guitar with a teacher who has Elvis Presley sideburns. He slides his fingers round the strings to create chords which I cannot imitate as it hurts too much. After some woeful attempts, which end each time with cries of 'Ohhh!', he suggests that I sing along to his playing. The sound is musical enough to encourage him to test my choral range. The man claims I have the choice of notes of an opera star. I blush furiously at the compliment. Is this a pick up line? Does Elvis Presley now intend to take me on his lap and ease down my trousers like Dad? But he doesn't. Instead he refers me to the choirmaster and my career begins at once. By the end of the second year I am singing most of the school solos.

Being a chorister, you are treated with a certain hushed respect by your peers as if you are in the personal hands of God. You may be attacked if you appear in sports clothes in a conveniently dark place but boys don't lay for you round every corner. One vengeful soul nevertheless dares to throw a compass at my back in Prep while the master's back is turned. It sticks between my shoulder blades like the knife in The Man Who Knew Too Much. I don't collapse like the Frenchman but simply gasp and turn white in the face. I reach behind and claw at the compass until I can pull it out. In chapel I process grandly down the aisle, dressed in a blue robe, white surplice and a dangling medal, with my hair neatly brushed. I look round to see if Dad is there and when he is, I smile winningly at the man. I can guess how proud and hot he's feeling; how he might wish to take me upstairs to the dormitory for a private cuddle. Am I being transformed into a servant of heaven or of hell? When I get home, I know my Dad will be teaching me new erotic tricks. Meanwhile the effect of united voices soaring to the rafters is uplifting. Parents sigh and think about the next term's cheque they will soon be writing. 'Ah, but it's so worthwhile to see the dear boy in his white ruff.' They wipe at their eyes with soft handkerchiefs.

The only place where reverence fails is with some of the wilder teachers in the classroom. There is a butch lady who stands me in the corner wearing a dunce hat because my handwriting heads uphill. There's a master who holds me back from seeing The Great Escape on Sunday because my Latin is not good enough. The French teacher indulges in a form of licensed sadism called Le Tour des Bicyclettes. He stands behind me when I fail to remember my French spelling and seizes me by the short hairs round the ears. He twirls the hairs on each side with such fast motion that I am lifted clean off the chair. While I am jerking like a marionette, he chants the correct spelling. 'Les cadeaux sont A-C-H-E-T-E-S!' Then he drops me back in my chair in disgust. The gym master enjoys watching us do press-ups while he peers closely underneath to see if any part of our undercarriage is touching the floor. If it does, he may lash at the backs of our legs with his hand.

The rakishly thin headmaster looks like death warmed up. He takes corporal punishment in deadly earnest. One week I am entered twice in the Black Book for running in the corridor outside his room and talking too loudly during break. I am called to visit the HM and he shows me a selection of polished canes in a display case next to the school cups. 'Which one shall I use on you, Robert?' he asks as if I have the same honour of choice as a duellist. I tremble as he unlocks the cabinet and produces a knobbly bamboo wand. The HM indicates a chair over which I should bend. He takes a few steps back and runs to make the strike. The cane stings my buttocks like a swarm of angry bees. He hits again. Three more angry slashes criss-cross and make a fiery griddle of my backside. Now, I think, my father won't kiss me in that spot again. He's too fastidious. The HM reminds me to say thank you as I stagger towards the door. I'd like to mutter something he will not expect. 'Thank you, sir. My Dad won't kiss my bum quite so often now.'

My questions for my parents are, why send me to a boarding school when I am already confused and disorientated? Is this a further lesson in being ready for whatever punishment the world can throw in my direction?

ONE: (Dad speaking) The boys in our family have always been sent away to school since the days of King Henry the second. It's a sign of ancestry and good breeding; the way a boy of any class develops spine. You may get dangled in the air by

31

the short and curlies but at least you will learn how to decline a French verb correctly. Think how important that will be in your later life. One ancestor of the Montagu clan brokered peace between two nations when he was still a teenager. Why? Because he was the only person present who could speak French. Consider the importance of maths when you need to divide a number; you might need it in a gaming club. Nations stand or fall on their knowledge of sports. Was it not Eton where Waterloo was won on the playing fields? Let it not be Robert who consigns Britain to the status of a third world country. You may think that eight and nine is a suitable age to curl up by the fire but it isn't. Alexander conquered the known world when he was hardly much older. Boys of eight and nine are being formed to be tested under cannon fire, not given raw pastry by the cook and speciality marzipan cakes by his mother. Train your mind and body! Fight for your virtue with your blood! Play cricket with a straight bat and swing at the ball until you die! Toughen up the sinews and summon up the blood - that's the English style.

TWO: Mum once told a friend when I was older that if the country went to war, she was ready to pitch her sons into battle. She looked like a Spartan mother as she thundered: 'I'd rather they came home ON their shields than UNDER them!' – meaning she would prefer us dead than in hiding. She had lost her brother – my only uncle on her side – on the last day of fighting in Italy during the second world war, shot through the stomach by a German soldier. Timmy was the centre of her universe. So I could understand her warlike feelings of vengeance against national enemies. The violence of prep schools hardly featured in comparison.

THREE: (Dad again) Do you think your parents have no greater purpose in life than to spend their time looking after you, no matter how much they love you? Do you realise just how hard we work? By breakfast time, already I have waded through a mountain of post. By eleven I have answered fifty letters and I am taking calls from adherents of some lost cause. By lunchtime I am in the Commons, if I am not at home touring the farms and talking with tenants about their leaking roofs. Do you need me to continue? Your mother has a more leisurely breakfast than I do. She enjoys her boudoir and a hot bath. She takes long calls while she is combing her hair, speaking to a certain lady with a French accent. She sprays herself all over with scent. The studio in the house is approached by ten o'clock with a full carton of cigarettes and a strong mug of coffee. Your mother may pick up a self portrait reflected in a mirror and continue to add paint to the haggard canvas while smoking a cigarette. More likely she will sort through old pictures standing against the wall, looking for a work she cares for. She may give it to a friend; certainly not sell it. These are more important activities than tending to the needs of a boy when he could be at school.

FOUR: (Dad) At a deeper level, do you think it's safe for me to keep my son around, knowing how you sometimes tempt me? No, it isn't. My only alternative is to thrust you far from view. I cannot allow you to come into constant contact or my love – whatever it is – will become uncontrollable. I will go beyond all bounds. In boarding school you are at least safe from such dangerous attention. I am freeing you by an act of selflessness. You are not even out of my mind when you are out of sight. I stare at that photo of you on my desk and sometimes start crying. I send frequent postcards to you written in turquoise ink. Once I sent a big photo of a submarine I had just inspected and a nuclear missile I had just been shown: neither image was at all permissible with the authorities concerned but it was sent to excite you and your friends. Fruit arrives at the school by special post, does it not? – hand-picked by me. What more tokens can I send of my extraordinary love, while stressing the importance of keeping well away?

I'd like to make some comments from my side if that's OK.

Sending me to boarding school makes me even more off-kilter with the world than I now am at home. I have already lost my sense of personal location; now I have lost my geographical bearings too. I am nervous, jittery, moving as if under watch and suffering from a series of deprivations. *Perhaps that has been deserved and God approves of my punishment.* I have allowed my father to touch me intimately, even if I have played no physical part. I am beginning to judge my mother because I see how contented she is with the women in her life. I feel the prickle of resentment against her and her girl-friends that I see on holidays; they are keeping my mother away from me which makes her unaware of the goings-on in Dorset. I am envious of my sisters, imagining they are having more fun than me. I have a strong sense that God has lost patience with me for lying in bed beside my father. That's why He has given me a French master who delights in *Le Tour des Bicyclettes*. That is why I have already been beaten by the HM with the knobbly cane.

At school my relationships with females have been annihilated. The only stand-in for my mother is a matron who leans over me with a tablespoon and force-feeds me malted syrup. When she is not occupied with that obsession, she is pushing my head underwater in the freezing cold while a line of naked shivering boys stretches far down the corridor. The matron steals quietly into my dormitory at night to catch me playing chess with my next door neighbour, leaning in our pyjamas over the side of our beds. She tans me four times on the buttocks with a leather-soled slipper while I bend across the bed frame. I have read stories since of how some men make life-time fetishes out of that sort of treatment. I am glad I don't feel any particular relish for being lashed by a woman.

Yes, it's true – these unpleasant elements are offset to some degree by joyful incidents in the holidays. These however seem to belong in a different world; one that somehow doesn't count. What is being missed while I am in school cannot be recovered. I have no idea what my sisters or my brother are up to as they are growing and as a result we grow up strangers. Think of it - if I see them even half the holidays, that's only six weeks a year; it comes down to less than an hour in every two hundred. What has gone on in their world I will never know, to say nothing of what's happening in my parents' lives: in politics or the studio, a smoke-filled salon or some slinky boudoir. I touch objects when I come home that I have never seen before. My mother has new friends that have become over-familiar. They stare at me with suspicion or fake interest. I feel they would prefer me to disappear.

I am supposed to view this schooling as a useful training for life. It is a part of growing up, of putting away childish things; it is also fearfully expensive. But a maturing influence is not being maintained when I return to my father's house, nor to my mother's for that matter. I am either fussed over as a child or largely ignored. Mum sings me nursery songs and music hall ditties when she comes to my room at night, usually half-drunk and slurping over me in a distasteful way I think may be erotic. One day I must ask her about that. Something is horribly awry at my father's house where I am not being treated normally. The hour or more spent inside his bedroom is starting to pull me to pieces. The worlds of normal and abnormal are colliding like planets in the sky.

Going back a little, my first memory of London is of a corridor. I am sitting in a playpen wearing a nappy. There is a little girl in there with me, about the same age as I am. She is the daughter of Mum's current girlfriend, though I don't know that yet. I know we are contented to be in the playpen together as we are giggling happily. I may even be pressing my toes against her leg. This is obviously not the corridor of the huge dark mansion belonging to my father. There are no nannies to be seen; certainly not my hair-lipped one. The furnishings are modern 1950s. Our mothers come into view at the far end of the corridor, talking and laughing. My mother's friend has a soft-skinned face and a commanding nose. The structure of her bones is striking with sky blue eyes under firm brows. I can tell the two adults are happy because there is a lot of smiling going on. Perhaps instinctively I can tell they are in love. I can see the indentation of lines round my mother's mouth. She is around 34. Her friend looks a lot younger than that.

While we sit in the playpen waggling our toes with our mothers watching, disaster strikes. A black Scottie dog races through the open doorway behind and makes for us down the corridor. His eyes are gleaming with hunger and the certainty of satisfying it. It is plain from his open jaws and slavering gums that he plans to eat *these succulent babes one by one. The only obstacles to success are the thin wooden bars of the playpen. The Scottie dog seizes the woodwork and worries at it as if he is chewing a bone. His eyes are as yellow as a demon's. Our mothers haul the snarling dog away, yelling at him to be silent. By that time both infants are screaming with trauma and clutching at each other for support. It's an interesting speculation that if our mothers had not separated us, we might have gone on cuddling all our lives. Then we would have had two couples clutching each other within the same family.*

I am back to seven or eight when I try the next phase in the interesting but strange and unusual process of male-female bonding. Until then our mothers have kept Alice and myself mostly apart. The girl lives with her mother in a house a good mile away. One day the four of us are having tea at home chez nous. I don't know where my sisters are but they are not present in this memory. Alice and I decide to lock ourselves in the lavatory and inspect each other's parts. I don't know how this decision is arrived at but it seems of mutual interest. The toilet is a small room on the first landing with a Victorian crapper that takes up half the space inside. I squeeze against the wall while this impish little miss with a Scottish accent pulls down her underpants and jumps up on the seat in her tartan skirt. It is the first sight I have been given of the pursed lips between a girl's thighs. How can pee come out of that closed orifice? I watch breathless as the slit opens at the front and a thick stream pulses out. So that is how it functions for a girl. It looks like there is a small hole above the main opening which is tight shut. The flow doesn't come from deep inside. Alice finishes and jumps down after wiping herself, pulling up her pants. She orders me to do the same. Feeling proud of my easier boy's performance, I face the toilet and unzip my trousers. The girl squirms against the wall to watch as I fish out my hooded penis and direct it at the water. The force and carry of the flow surprises Alice and she gasps as she opens her eyes wide.

'You can do it like that, standing up?' she whispers in awe. 'That's amazing!'

'Sure,' I boast, waggling my willy to shake off the drops. 'That's why a boy's thing is made this way, so he can pee without having to sit down.'

It doesn't occur to me there may be other purposes for the tube; this one is sufficient in itself. Alice reaches out a hand to touch the silken shaft before it disappears back inside my pants. I am wondering if she is checking out if the tube is made of skin and not plastic when there comes the sound of vexed voices outside the door and the handle is tested.

'Who's in there?' a stern voice demands: it's Alice's Mum. 'Open up.'

I can hear my own mother in the background muttering.

'It's me,' Alice says.

'Are you on your own? Where's Robert?'

I have to declare my presence; otherwise under all rules of schoolboy conduct I would be beyond the pale.

'I'm in here as well.'

'Why? What are you doing together?'

'Nothing!'

At this point it's my mother who takes over yanking at the door handle.

'Come out of there, both of you. Unlock the door this minute,' she orders.

As soon as the door opens, my mother hauls me out and slaps me hard across the cheek and once more across the bum.

'What do you think you're doing, you disgusting boy?'

'Were you touching each other?' Alice's mother is yelling in her daughter's face.

'No,' the girl lies.

We are hauled apart and I am banished to my room. Later on I can hear in the distance my friend crying but I cannot bring comfort to her. My impression is the next time we meet, we are already grown. Alice's pretty freckles have vanished. The girl is interested only in much older boys. We meet in Scotland when I am about fourteen. I hope for romantic walks but none are on offer. I sit alone and listen to the sound of the Corryvreckan whirlpool roaring at unwary sailors.

So my questions for Mum and Dad are obvious – chiefly for my Mum this time. Why lock away at eight the only girl in my line of sight? What were your reasons for doing that? Could it be that you were scared of the idea of us falling in love when that seemed the prerogative of yourself and her mother?

ONE: (Mum) Girls and boys of any age only get together in a lavatory for a sexual purpose.

That's clear and unequivocal. So it's sensible when they show interest to keep an eye on them to stop that happening. If children are left together in such a place, they will touch each other and one thing will lead to the next. That's logical. Boys cannot keep their hands to themselves; girls are curious by nature. Consequently it's vital to keep the mind occupied at all times with WHOLESOME THOUGHTS. The only activities in touching that should be allowed are things like cooking together, picking flowers or shrimping in the Isle of Wight. Leave the exploration of the body for later days when the person is searching for experimentation.

TWO: The best answer to sexual activity is to leave it to mature judgement. Don't influence the gender issue by encouraging boys and girls to enter lavatories. Look what happened to me: I was committed to a man in his mid twenties by an engagement at seventeen. Men can be inconstant, selfish brutes with natural insensitivity. Their main interest is to create slaves to manage their desires. Pretty girls like Alice should be allowed to grow up free so they can choose to bond with whoever they desire, whether male or female.

THREE: Yes, I did keep you somewhat apart after the shock of seeing you together like that. Do you think it was appropriate for you and Alice to be touching each other at the same time as us? *That's insane!* No wonder I whacked you across the cheek. It's perverse to even think such thoughts. I shouldn't wish to continue being your mother if

41

that went on. It may surprise you, Robbo, but I was properly brought up.

Now it's my turn for a comment, Mamma.

Your morality leaps all over the place. It's all right for you to leave my father when I'm five and take to women but it's wrong for me to look at a naked girl at eight. What kind of logic is that? You wouldn't have taken that view if you'd stayed at home. Without your girlfriend present – if we'd still been in the big old house with servants and a father wearing an orchid in his button-hole – you would have stood back from the loo door and laughed. You have enough democratic principle in you for that. Perhaps you wouldn't have allowed us to remain on the toilet but you wouldn't have slapped me. That was because it was a personal affront. Your questionable morality was showing there; your – dare I say – uncertain sense of right that what you were doing was correct.

I managed a bit of a slaughter this morning because it repelled me to see the line of ants marching across the kitchen floor, making a beeline for the larder. Father Perceval keeps our bread in there and sugar and cheese and fruit. The ants seem to like the sugar as they climb the walls and shelves in a straight line towards it and chuck themselves in the bowl as if the crystals were a honey bath. You swipe them off with a dishcloth and they hesitate a moment as if surveying the ruin of the world and then come on, grinning as if to say, 'You didn't think you could get rid of us so easily?'

What I did was to get down from the top shelf a bottle of pink paraffin that we have and lay a trail across the floor from the hall where they get in past the lintel of the front door. I lit it with a match like a fuse and watched the blue flames race along the floor, incinerating the column of ants in their path like a death ray. I don't know what that did for my psyche but I sure as hell had to spend the next hour cleaning up so Father P wouldn't notice the burn marks on the floor.

One Sunday at home in Dorset when I am nine my father asks me to sing an anthem in the private chapel adjoining the house. There is a crowd of tenant farmers and their children coming. I guess he wants to show that we are as Christian as anyone. He wants the solo to be 'Lead me, Lord' by Samuel Wesley, which happens to be a piece I have sung to the whole school. I practise the opening bars a few times in the library next door to the chapel. Dad fingers the notes on the piano with watering eyes. When I sing the words during the service, my father's eyes are on me all the time and they are watering like mad. This makes me nervous. If Dad starts to cry, people will begin wondering what's the matter. Does his son cause this degree of emotion in him and for what reason?

    'Lead me, Lord,
Lead me in Thy righteousness,
Make Thy way plain
Be...fore my face.'

My eyes are clear but troubled. The Lord's way is not plain to me in any form. I haven't a clue how He wants me to behave towards my father when we are upstairs. My Dad's eyes sag under a weight of pouches. Is this caused by parliamentary business or by his guilt over his treatment of me?

'For it is Thou, Lord,
Thou Lord only
That makest me dwell
In sa...fety.'

Dad falls to his knees in prayer at the end of the an-
them when I return to my place. What's he praying to God
so busily for? What will be the answer? The priest leaves a
small silence at the end of prayers and I see my father rub-
bing his fists deeply into his eyes which is probably how he
got them so puffy in the first place. Is he feeling gripped by
remorse? Is he anguished by this mad humour of love busi-
ness? Maybe he is regretful and will stop my visits to his
room which are still going on and getting more intense day
by day. Unless it is the thought that he has not reminded
Cook to put treacle on the sponge pudding.

My subject for today is, what part does God or Christ play in our morning ritual? My father appears to be a God-fearing man – I think he would have it so - and yet his touching has progressed steadily over the last two years. He now moves behind me when I am lying naked on my front and mimics the action of making love. He has plumped up my bottom with a pillow to have better access to my rump. He covers his penis with a handkerchief – I never see the organ itself - and rides the phallus up and down my arse until he emits a groan and spills into the handkerchief. I am never touched by the liquid, only the sensation of heat.

I thought one of the main points of Christianity – of any religion – is to convey the need for contain-

45

ment. I think most people would agree with me that my Dad has gone far beyond that. Something inside him has gone haywire. Is God failing to deliver to him a message of caution? I'm not physically hurt, only distressed by the steady growth of his passion. The feelings are mixed and internal. I am aware that what Dad is doing is wrong. He has gone beyond social norms. I know that is so from the whispering that goes on among schoolboys about cocks and apertures and vaginas. Dad is showing love of a kind *but of what variety and why so much?* Does the word love cover his panting? Perhaps I should not lie still but roll away; there is a duty on me of non-compliance. Am I acting sinfully by not running away?

So Dad, it's time for more response from you.

ONE: You have to realise, boy, how hard God was actually working to limit my acts against you. If it had not been for His constant whispering, my liberties would have gone much further, with no limit on the time of day. There is no excuse for that and I am not attempting to give you one. I was missing your mother and you were her substitute. But don't blame God or His angels for the lack of good advice. They prevented my acts from becoming more extreme and there were occasions – not a great number, I grant you – when I left you alone entirely. To take one example, I never brought you into my bed on skiing trips. Isn't that correct? Will you kindly remind our Lord of that forbearance on the day we come to judgement?

TWO: I have been given by society a certain latitude because of my position, as if have said before – both as a member of parliament and a Lord of the realm. I don't make a habit of boasting but it's true: you can ask anyone to confirm my status. Who is the number one person in the country? The Queen. After her comes the social hierarchy and if you look up in Debrett's or Burke's Peerage, you will find my place firmly written near the top. I'm a close friend of members of the Cabinet. At least one member of the royal family is a relation. We are descended from kings ourselves. This gives me a certain entitlement to decide the doings in my life. Who is the natural head of a family? It's the father, the *pater familias*. He is the nearest thing to God that we know apart from the Archbishop. His commandments are in a sense both God's and the community's. I make the rules and you stick by them. That includes making me content in any way I please.

THREE: There is no devil buried inside me, only an excess of exuberant spirits created by circumstance and tradition. There are many men like me and more in each generation: one reason is that we tend to spread our favours about. What we do together is not at all *unusual or devious*. If it was, wouldn't I order you to keep silent? The fact is, I have never done so. Nor would I defend a man who did. I don't subscribe to dictatorship. The fact is you are free to tell your story to anyone you like. I would of course deny it but that is my privilege. What we have between us is called a tacit understanding. It's an agreement that needs no written contract, nor even words. I ask your permission for my acts by reaching for you with my hands. You give me what I want as you are my loving son. No words are needed; in fact they are de trop.

FOUR: To be totally honest, there is an additional reason why I go to church. I have confessed this reason to God and He understands it. Churches are places where children such as you are often members of the congregation. I can be sure there will be many adolescent boys there who will look like their mothers. Westminster Abbey near my home in London is a good case in point. Boys flood in from the school passages and there are always choristers sitting in the stalls who stir my heart to frenzy. A long procession marches past when I attend as I do regularly. Creatures like you dressed in their fine robes turn my head and make it spin like a top. I hope I am not being disloyal by revealing this. I suppose what I am trying to say is that if you did decide to remain in your own bed before breakfast, I'd soon replace you with another special boy. I don't mean to sound callous but it's true.

I have now grown up with church music and choirs for a period of eight years. I have listened to hundreds of sung eucharists and chanted prayers. I can recite many of them from memory. But mixed with awe at this splendour is the taste of something sour. God knew my father's antics and his mind and yet He didn't put a stop to them. If I believe in the goodness of God and His existence, then I must believe He is NOT all-powerful. Perhaps it is an error to think that God can change anything by action. It is an error put about by priests who love the mystery of religious power. Perhaps the reality is that God is a force that has no physical dimension. We must reject all religious teaching that tells us otherwise. The alternative to that is not to believe in God's existence and lose faith altogether.

Father Perceval challenged me this morning before he went off to Rome.

He said, 'It's true you came into the city and stopped moping around the castle.' He added, 'It's also time you did some shopping for redecorations.' I asked huffily, which did he want me to do first? He said, 'You can walk with me down the hillside and we'll choose a colour for some paint before I catch my train.'

The man behind the counter at the *mesticheria* hadn't a clue what we were looking for until I made a hand gesture, pretending I had a brush and was repainting his counter.

'Ah…*vuole vernice!*' the man guessed.

He produced a colour chart which had a hard white and various shades of cream and grey. Father P was interested in a bluish tint that verged on lilac. I shook my head and told him I refused point blank to paint such a gay colour. The shoppers behind us took a close interest in our choice; whether this was due to concern for the ruined castle or fascination over the antics of the mad monk and his protégé I wasn't sure. The queue committee decided there was no other choice than an off white colour like chalk. Anything else would upset the owner and also local historical sensitivities. A weighty six litres of the stuff was fetched from the back room and a roller and a paint tray; also a heap of rags suitable for washing down walls and sheets of sandpaper for scraping off flaky paint.

Father P stomped off to catch the train when he was satisfied with what we'd bought with my mother's money.

'*Allora torna subito al castello, giovanotto?*' the shopkeeper asked when I turned to leave.

'What's that you say?'

'You walk back now to the castello?'

I nodded. What else could I do: transport myself there on a magic carpet?

'*Giuseppe…*' The man turned to his assistant, possibly his son. '*Portami il raggazzo su al castello con la macchina.*'

I didn't know what he meant until the assistant ushered me outside and into a nearby car. I gushed my thanks all the way up the hill, thinking what a climb it would have been carrying those heavy cans of paint. A bit like Sisyphus pushing his stone up the hill only to have it roll back downwards. I might have dropped a tin and watched it roll until it smashed into some house wall. That would have given me some personal satisfaction, seeing the paint explode and spray go everywhere. My psyche would have gone *Hurray – that's what you should be doing to yourself. Why don't you just roll down the hillside and smash against the wall?*

I have a good friend at school called Walter who is a specialist at running away. The trouble is he keeps getting caught. He has been punished by the headmaster so many times his bum is beginning to look like a griddled steak. I tell Walter he should report the HM to the police for crimes against humanity but he simply grins and whispers me the plan for his latest escape attempt.

'Next time I'm heading for a bus,' Walter says. 'I've been caught so many times walking across the fields or down the main road. I swear the HM has briefed the citizens of Oxford to look out for me. On a bus, you've got the right to be there, provided you have money for the fare.'

'Do you have the money?' I ask.

'Sure.' Walter shows me a ten shilling note. 'Got it sent by my father.'

I know this escape plan is going to be no different from the others. The bus conductor will turn him in or else the driver will. Walter is one of those guys who will keep escaping until he is thrown into a tin hut like a prisoner of war; otherwise his Mum will take pity on him and haul him back to London. Still the boy's good humour is a useful lesson to stay bright whatever the situation and so I stick around him as much as possible to learn about survival techniques.

'Why do you want to escape?' I ask, thinking it is what I should be doing.

'Cos I like it better in London.'

'What do you like there?'

'I can see my mates. Also I enjoy the spying game.'

Walter lives with his mother and sister in a small house in Belgravia. I know because I have visited there in the holidays and seen the place: the stale milk standing in the hallway, the uncollected mail that Walter says are demands for money, the unmade beds upstairs. His mother lives with a man who works as a spy spotter. He reports to MI5 where the Russian spooks are living – they generally like homes round Knightsbridge – then he goes to the Russian embassy and tells them where the MI5 officers are staying who are watching them. He makes good money from both sides.

Walter is caught and beaten once again after the bus ride. This time he's not grinning so much when he comes out of the HM's study. He has to visit the matron where she dabs cotton wool and antiseptic on his rear. When I visit him in sick bay, Walter tells me what he's planning to do to the headmaster's perfect lawn outside his study window when he has the chance.

'What's that?'

'I'm going to sow a mass of stones under his grass,' he says.

'What's the good in that?'

'The stones will grow into mountains, silly, and the HM won't be able to see out.'

I shake my head. Oh dear, it's another of Walter's plans.

During the next holidays when we are ten, we go down to Dorset together to visit my father's house. I have filled my friend's head with promises of spying on the guests. Dad often invites young couples he has met for a romantic weekend. I think he enjoys watching their amorous courting as much as we do. I reckon if we follow them closely round the garden, we can watch them kissing. This idea works a treat and we spend a heap of time watching which way the noses go when their mouths are locked together. Well, it's a serious problem for a nose.

First thing in the morning I lie in bed and wonder if I will go to my father's room as usual or else wait for Walter to come in. I know Dad will be waiting for me and looking at his watch. Will he be cross later if I don't appear? He may be. But I don't wish to miss any time with my friend. Walter will want to get dressed and go exploring, being the adventurous kind of boy he is. Eventually I knock on his door to wake him up.

'Hello. Come in,' he says, sitting up in bed.

'Do you want to get dressed and do something before breakfast?' I ask. 'Otherwise I'll pop down the corridor and visit my Dad, which I do often.'

Walter looks at me with his head cocked on one side as if I'm barmy.

'You go into his bedroom? Why?'

'Because he likes me to visit him.'

'For how long?'

'Sometimes an hour. He reads me stories and we play games.'

Walter makes a face.

'What kind of games?'

'Oh…games.'

'Aren't you getting a bit old for that?' he asks.

I shrug. 'Maybe. But Dad gets grumpy if I don't go.'

Walter considers me carefully. I wonder if he's working things out a little in his mind. However this is a boy who thinks that stones grow into mountains.

'Let's do something different,' he suggests. 'You can get your Dad to blame me if you like. Let's go up on the roof and peer over the edge. It's exciting and there may be something interesting to see. We might see something through a window. Or else we can climb a tree.'

'I know what,' I say. 'I'll show you a fence we can walk along. Let's see if you can go from one end to the other along the top without falling off.'

We dress quickly and run downstairs, waving hello to the cook who is rolling out the pastry. I stop to grab a handful and pass some on to Walter. The fence runs along the rear courtyard past the house. There is a wooden gate halfway along. The rail is two inches wide. I give a demonstration of rail walking in my sneakers. All the time I am thinking of my father listening to the radio, looking at his watch and scratching his head. He will be wondering why I have not joined him. Has he been abandoned? Will Dad work out that I am distracted because I am with my friend? Walter follows me along the fence rail.

'Let's make it more dangerous,' he suggests after a time. 'Let's take a bite out of the wood with an axe. Then you have to walk along the rail blind-folded and see if you fall.'

I know that Dad will be furious if he sees we have chopped a piece out of his fence. So what if he is? It's the first rebellious thought that has crossed my mind as far as he is concerned. It must be the influence of Walter. I can hear Dad's busy panting behind my shoulders. We would have reached the point if I was with him when… well, you know what I mean. I think with relish, for once I will deny his pleasure. We search out a hatchet from the wood shed. Walter cuts a V-shaped chunk from the fence with the blade, narrowing the rail to half the width. He's going to make a second cut in another place but I stop him from doing that.

'One cut's enough.'

We walk the gauntlet in turn, turning up our heads to face the sky and wobbling as we pass the cut. By the time we've done the walk twice without incident, it's time for breakfast; too late to hare down the corridor to my father's room and splutter my apologies. He arrives at breakfast with the expected severe frown at my innocent expression.

'What happened to you, boyzo?'

'I was with Walter.'

'Oh!' Dad shows his woe-begotten face. 'I was forgetting you had a friend you might want to be with.'

The odd thing is that next time I go to my father's house, I try walking that fence again instead of visiting him. I don't look down because I am thinking so hard about not being in his bed: you might say tossing up the virtues and the disadvantages. Suddenly I miss my step in the cut-out V and fall astride the rail, whacking my prick, my balls and forehead hard on the edge. I tip over and land in a thick clump of nettles, roaring with pain in a variety of places, chiefly between my legs. I run at a limp for the house and fall screaming on the sofa in the sitting-room, with blood running from my forehead, feeling that my guts are turning inside out. My calls bring my sister Kate racing from upstairs. She tends me until my Dad arrives.

'What's happened?' he cries, falling on his knees. 'I was waiting for you, boy. You didn't come.'

'I was out walking on a fence,' I cry. 'Then I fell astride the rail and off into a clump of nettles.'

My Dad understands where I have been hurt by the way I have screwed my thighs tight shut. He wants to take down my trousers and pants for an examination but I am too ashamed to allow him to do that in front of my sister. Actually I am ashamed of the whole idea. There's been enough activity down there. I don't want him even to look in that direction.

'Leave me.' I push Dad's hand away as he explores.

'Call for the doctor,' orders Kate who is by now fifteen. 'Meanwhile I'll stay with Robert.'

When Dad has gone, I allow my sister to examine the savagely aching place. After all she has washed me often enough in the past, playing the part of mum. There's not been much physical growth since she last handled my testicles. Her fingers feel the bulbous shapes are still intact, not squashed flat as a pancake. Maybe I will still be able to make babies when the time comes.

'It hurts where exactly? Here…?'

'Yes!' I yell. 'And there and there!'

Meanwhile I am thinking I have been surely punished by God for failing to visit my Dad. The one time I make a challenge and don't appear – when I follow my friend's advice – what happens? I fall astride a fence and hurt myself seriously. There is no question whose side God is on – my Dad the interferer's. My duty is to continue doing my job as long as he needs me in his bed. Forget the rebellion.

I have to admit there is another time of day when we are together and I have never objected: in the bathroom. I haven't talked about that yet. Every evening Dad pours himself and his guests a cocktail: usually a vodka martini with a green olive popped in the middle of the glass. Before he comes upstairs, Dad puts on some classical music on his record player in a hall cupboard; always with a full orchestra playing and people singing such as in Wagner. The sound echoes round the house through speakers in the hallway upstairs. While Dad undresses in his room, I do the same inside mine and slip along the passage in my dressing gown. We meet in his cream pile-carpeted bathroom, walled with pictures of stuffed exotic birds. Dad moves a screen across the open door so he can hear the music without guests seeing us in the bath. He takes off his robe and steps inside the steaming water. It is the only time of day I see him fully naked: as red as a lobster from gardening, with wrinkled genitals and a flabby bum. As he settles down, I step in as well, sitting as always with my back to him and leaning back until he holds me in his arms. I am aware of the jelly-like parts by my backside but I am used to those; also the breasts are slightly enlarged, pressing against my shoulder blades. I eat the olive and Dad finishes the vodka martini, putting the glass down with a sigh and a smack of the lips.

He washes himself down with soap while intoning the music we are hearing and sometimes repeating the German words of the opera. He loves the sound of the schichen and the schechen and the sprecken. When he has finished, he begins to wash my back, starting with my head and working downwards. When my waist is done, he asks me to kneel upright. His hands wash my backside and carefully between the cleft. Then he asks me to turn round and face him. The hands pass my genitals through a close inspection as he washes and I am talking about a few inches from his eyes. On the day of the accident, the balls are treated like rare birds' eggs in a nest: probably a million pounds' worth.

'Does that still hurt, boyzo?'

'Ouch, yes!'

'Don't worry, poppet, your balls will be fine. The skin doesn't even look red.'

Dad peels back the foreskin on my penis as he always does so he can wash inside the flap all round.

'See? No redness there or damage at all. All is as it should be, Robbo.'

He closes me up and I turn and settle once again between his thighs. We listen to more music until Dad sighs and says it's time to get out. He lifts the ancient Victorian cylinder that stoppers the drain and turns it to one side where there is a catch. We watch the water settle steadily in the bath like the level in a canal lock when it is being drained. When the liquid begins *to make a sucking sound, Dad lifts me out by the waist, giving my bottom a quick kiss as it passes by.*

'There, you're done. Now dry yourself and pass me the other towel, will you, boyzo.'

He stands as I wrap the towel round his middle and steps out.

My questions for today are mainly for myself.

Why didn't I keep up the rebellion once it started? Why did I permit the bathing ritual to continue? Why didn't I tell anyone what was happening, even so far as giving a hint, e.g. Wally or Kate or Mum? Why didn't I simply say no to my father's wishes: no morning performance, no touchy-feely baths, no contact with my body whatsoever, thanks very much?

ONE: I felt guilty at the thought of stopping my Dad's pleasure; also a little worried in case he got cross. There was a sense of duty and I guess a degree of excitement too. My thinking might have gone, *Dad is prepared to do THAT to me? It must be incredibly important to him, as important as dining with the queen. I owe it to him to go along.*

TWO: The bath ritual had become a fixed routine. I reckoned there couldn't be much harm in it if Dad was prepared to leave the door open. He didn't mind in principle if anyone looked in. Besides, I wouldn't clean myself properly if I was left to do the job alone. I was lazy with hygiene. Also it's a satisfying feeling to be washed like a mini emperor by the man who occupies the role as father. How many boys would have told him to get lost?

THREE: Telling anyone would mean the whole world finding out. The information couldn't be rationed. I knew from school experience how gossip flows so easily from a simple story. 'Your Dad's a politician and an aristocrat and he's doing THAT to you? Wait until I tell Henry and Dave. Wait until I tell my parents.' If I had told Walter what my Dad was up to on my visits, the news would have gone round the school in a flash, best friend or not. There would have been a hushed silence as I walked up the aisle in church, with the boys thinking, 'Montagu doesn't deserve his position in the choir. He lets his Dad fiddle with his bottom. He should be sent to an institution.'

FOUR: I didn't say no because I was partly enjoying the experience. What Dad was doing didn't hurt. All it felt was odd and wrong, but slightly delicious at the same time. The caressing, the sense of being loved – who would push that experience away? Besides, who was I to say no to him? A squirt of a second son, the last in a long line of offspring. What Dad was doing for me was considerable: feeding me, giving me a place to sleep, paying for all my education, my clothes and holidays. All I had to do in return was turn up for the morning and evening ritual during which I did nothing. I should remember – as teachers regularly reminded us – how many people in the world there are who don't get a square meal, who don't have a bed or a roof or a school to go to. So who owes to who in this equation? Me – I'm the one who owes my Dad.

Those tins of paint stared at me all day and made me feel guilty when I did nothing about them. Father Perceval made it worse when he arrived this evening and saw I had done nothing. Consequently I spent an hour promising him that tomorrow I would start scrubbing down the dormitory upstairs and scraping away old paint so I can begin the decorations. At least I would not be accused of spending ANOTHER DAY being idle.

The day after tomorrow the mad monk has persuaded me to leave my lair and visit Rome. We'll split up once we've arrived and meet up for lunch at this bar where he has organized the group of lads to perform in public. If it sounds dire – Elvis Presley mixed with seaside Italian crooners and English rock and roll – I'm allowed to walk out but Father P is so excited by the thought that he is wetting his pants. It's exactly this sort of enthusiasm for *performance* that got us involved in the first place: Father P desperate to go down on his knees beside boys in trouble. I was still living down his Kiss of Peace service at the school this summer. Some boys at Eton thought I had brought him to the place myself. Where did you dream up the Franciscan friar? they asked me. *I didn't ask for him,* I told them. *The school decided to bring him in, not me.*

I have this faint scar running at an angle by my eyebrow where the doctor who came to my Dad's house stitched me up. It looks piratical like a quirk or question mark and Walter at school makes a constant joke of it. Then an odd thing happens during the summer holidays when Walter next comes to stay. It proves that divine intervention exists and God is taking a close interest in my affairs. We are in the Isle of Wight, standing in a chestnut tree in a fork between two branches, clearing away some smaller branches from the line of sight of my brother's window. John who is now 17 has a girl in there, a pretty French one with a slinky figure. He has turned out tall, chestnut-haired and reasonably good-looking. We suspect that my brother is diddling this girl morning, noon and night but we may be totally wrong. It is our detective duty to find out.

My machete severs the first branch. It falls from the tree and smashes to the ground. The second blow cuts through a similar branch but then goes smack into Walter's forehead, creating an identical wound to the one I received falling astride the fence. This time it's my friend who topples out of the tree and smashes to the ground. Thinking I have killed him, I jump down and yell for help as I wipe away the welling blood. My inner voice is telling me this blow is pre-ordained. It is a lesson to us both from the Almighty not to oppose my father.

The ambulance arrives, bells screaming, and men carry away Walter with his head bandaged. My sisters hover over him in a protective cortege. I feel a moment's envy as the French girl leans down and wishes him good luck with a tender kiss. She doesn't give one to me. My sisters look at me accusingly when Walter has left the scene. They are fond of my handsome friend.

'Didn't you THINK at all?' my mother is hissing. 'Didn't it occur to you that your hatchet might miss the tree and hit poor Walter in the head?'

'It didn't miss,' I claim. 'It went THROUGH the branch and then hit his head.'

Some important difference. My brother looks at me disgustedly as if I'm trying to boast. I just don't want to be accused of a poor aim. The hospital calls to say Walter has been stitched up and is sitting in bed hoping for visitors.

That summer the girls decide to camp out on the lawn inside a tent they have put up. The canvas territory is out of bounds to small boys. The older ones have their boyfriends and they are jiving to the sound of rock and roll. The air in the sitting room fills with cigarette smoke. My mother has locked herself in the kitchen with her friends, preparing the ingredients for supper. When Walter returns from hospital, we go for recuperative walks along the beach with the girls staring after us enviously. We discover a World War 2 bomb buried in the sand and tell the police about it.

I am feeling oddly separated from the mainstream of life and wish to tell Walter the truth about my Dad. I need to unburden my soul and take the pressure off myself. Do I dare to do so? Dad hasn't asked for secrecy. Walter might be persuaded to hold his tongue. However there is a heavy burden on me of silence. I guess I am ashamed of the truth; also no one would be happy with my revelation. My mother has firmly locked the door of her kitchen. My sisters have sealed up the tent. My brother has barricaded his bedroom door. We all have our own spaces and don't wish to be invaded by some-one else's stuff.

My father visits us in the Isle of Wight one warm summer's day when Parliament is in recess. He is wearing his usual button-hole and a crumpled white suit with a Panama hat. He is perspiring freely when we meet on Ryde pier and mops his brow with a large white handkerchief – one I am only too familiar with. I am wearing light blue shorts with sandals and a thin tee shirt. He looks me up and down with a critical eye as if he might comment on my clothes. Instead he hugs me fiercely and whispers hot words of love. When we arrive home, I watch as the same critical eye takes in the cracks in the woodwork, the peddle-dash finish to the house and the flaking paint. My mother has no staff to attend to such matters and cares little for convention. I wince as my antediluvian father is met by the lively teenagers in the family and their sexy partners. He frowns to see one sister tickling her boyfriend under the chin.

My mother acts coquettish and has brushed her hair into a wave. She introduces her current half Greek

girlfriend who combs her long dark hair with her fin-
gers. Our family doctor is among the guests. He makes
manly conversation with my father about plants with
Latin names while the girls bring in canapés, walking
on bare feet across the floorboards. Lunch is a lobster
salad with crabs, mussels and prawns thrown haphaz-
ardly into the dish. My father picks at the spread as if
he has been invited to a sheikh's tent in the Arab desert
and may be asked to eat sheep's eyes. Meanwhile other
family members reach and grab morsels from the dish,
stripping the prawns from their casing with practised
ease and dropping them in their mouths between greasy
fingers.

'Hinch, what do you think of Macmillan's posture
on nuclear disarmament?' the doctor asks down the
table.

My father eyes the man carefully before using his
large handkerchief to clean his lips. He launches into
a long exposition of the fact that the nuclear threat is
the only sure deterrent against a new World War. My
older sisters shake their heads in uneasy disagreement.
My mother decides she will not allow these words to
go unchallenged. I recognise the spots of colour in her
cheeks. Please don't argue, I urge her with my eyes, but
of course she doesn't pay attention. As the argument
flares up and becomes more heated, Dad's face goes stiff
as if he is being punched repeatedly below the belt. His
eyes cast round as if they might light on someone who
could order this unruly woman to hold her tongue. My
eldest sister Sarah stands with her fuzz of curly hair
and seizes an unopened bottle of white wine. She points

it cradled under her arm like a machine-gun at both our parents and starts to fire.

'Pop-pop-pop-pop-pop-pop…'

Dad leaves soon after lunch, pleading the long journey back to Dorset. I go with him to see him off while a sister drives.

'So unfortunate to have an argument today of all days,' he mutters, using his handkerchief to wipe his forehead. 'I never intended such a thing. But your mother will pick on the smallest details. She has such strong opinions.'

I wonder who has taught her to debate except my father. My sister Anne makes a forgiving comment on both positions. She is not the one who sprayed our parents with machine-gun fire. I stay quiet. My father turns and grins at me in the seat behind.

'At least you won't abandon me, will you, Robbo? Come and see me before you go back to school. Promise.'

Rightly speaking I should say no.

'Of course I will,' I reply instead with enthusiasm.

Before the end of August, I return to Dorset. The days are devoted to my wishes. We picnic often on a neighbour's land where Dad creates his own domain by driving without permission through a farmer's fields. He cheerfully orders me to open the PRIVATE – NO ACCESS gate as if he has feudal rights to go where he wishes. That's an interesting proof of his world philosophy.

Down in the woods at the stream half a mile from the house, he suggests I take off my clothes and bathe in the water. I strip off and pick my way carefully across the grass, anxious to avoid pine needles in my feet. Dad won't go in himself but enjoys watching my sylvan exercise. He grunts as my bottom touches the icy stream bed.

'Cold enough for you, boyzo?'

'Freezing.'

'Gets your circulation going, eh?'

I sit on the pebbled bed and allow the current to swirl round my ankles and belly, listening to the gurgle as the water finds its way downstream. The woods have that profound silence as if the trees are listening to the conversation between us. I stand up dripping and Dad opens wide his arms with the towel for me to rush over for a rubdown. Am I delaying growing up by enjoying this childish attention? Am I calling what is between us love? Or is it love that has turned into something else?

One afternoon before I return to school, I am passing a boring hour before tea when I spy my father clipping a yew hedge on a step ladder, using an electric trimmer and wearing a worn garden hat. He is hot in the face in the same way as he is during the morning exercise. An idea comes into my mind to startle him with a stone whizzing by into the bushes. From a distance, hidden behind a stone wall, I whizz a pebble towards the man. In mid-flight the stone sways and shifts, flying closer and closer to my father's head. It strikes him on the temple below the rim of the hat and he bellows, falling off the ladder. Mercifully the hedge clipper is at that moment not in use.

I don't see more as I have crouched behind the wall but a few seconds later I hear Dad calling my name.

'Is that you, Robert? Did you throw that stone? Show yourself, wherever you are.'

I peep out to see my father standing, casting his eyes around with one hand rubbing his brow with the familiar white handkerchief.

'Did you throw that stone?' he thunders when he sees me.

'Yes, I did. Sorry, Dad. I didn't mean to hit you. Really I didn't.'

Did I not?

'Come over here, boy, and say you're sorry to my face.'

I think I will be beaten with his large square hand: a fate which has never befallen me before, except once when I made rings round him in excitement before a departure. As I approach, I hang my head and shuffle slowly.

'Sorry. I only meant to scare you.'

Dad rubs my head as if I am a wild animal and holds me close to his chest.

'Darling, it only just missed my eye.'

'I know it did.'

'Why should you want to scare me?'

Oh why? Oh why?

If I had fractured the skull or taken out an eye, would a part of me have been celebrating? I don't think so. I guess more likely I would have felt horribly guilty. However some resistance was obviously taking shape. The stream visit with me displaying myself like an attractive water sprite could be counted as a step in the other direction. You could call that a developing Narcissus complex if you wanted to sound professional.

ONE: Maybe I was scared by how far all this was going. What would happen if my Dad decided to throw away his handkerchief one fine day and complete his movements without the use of it? Maybe that would be the moment when my compliance would be tested to its limit. Maybe someone would walk in and see us together with me being ridden like a horse. I might forget to lock the door. Or else maybe some mysterious accident would befall my father with a stone.

TWO: I guess by that stage – ten – there was some pressure of physical development building inside me. Any time soon my body might begin to sprout. What new stages would I go through then? Would I be tempted to respond to his various movements? If I did, would Dad go on with our relationship or cease? He might be waiting eagerly for that change. He might be hoping soon I could play an active part in our activities.

THREE: I was beginning to realise that what was happening was going to affect my life for many years. I might start thinking this was fun and something to be looked for and repeated with other people. When I met a girl, I might start thinking more about her bottom than her front. Worse still, I might want to find a boy and experiment with him.

It was late afternoon when I faced the task of rubbing down the walls of the large dormitory, taking off the cobwebs and the flaky paint without bringing down the plaster. It took me half an hour to lay out newspaper to protect the old terracotta floor arranged in that herring bone design. The pages of the paper were filled with lurid descriptions of a series of murders with photos of the places where they happened. Girls strangled and left naked on a pile of leaves. The photos didn't exactly show the bodies but they did show the marks on the leaves.

The buckets of warm water had to be carried upstairs from the sink in the kitchen: the only place for hot water apart from the shower which only worked when the cylinder warmed up. I had to use the water sparingly or risk the plaster coming loose so I rinsed and squeezed out the rags each time before applying them. The dirt that came off the walls looked like scum from centuries of dust. Water dribbled down like rain on a window, forcing me to go back and dry it before continuing.

After another hour I'd gone all round the walls up to waist height and it was only then I started thinking how to clean the top section. Wouldn't it have been more sensible if I'd started from the ceiling and worked my way down? But I hadn't and the light was growing poor. The sky was dark and it was getting set to rain. I was cold and miserable and wanted a cup of tea, so I decided to call it quits. Soon Father Perceval would be getting back. At least I could say that I had started and would go on once we returned from Rome tomorrow.

I went downstairs and made myself a cup of tea, sipped it in front of the fire that I prepared and lit. So Rome next day and no writing! For once I could take a break before the next big moment arrived in the story. How I wish it had all been a fairy tale. I would have swopped my part for Cinderella's any time.

My Dad and I are going skiing for ten days before term begins in January. I have just turned eleven. We are going to visit a chalet at Wengen where I have not been before. The last night in England I am spending with him in Westminster so we are ready to leave early in the morning.

I go to his house after tea with my suitcase, dropped off by my Mum in a taxi. Dad tells me we are going out to a smart restaurant later. We'll take a bath first and change into evening clothes in case there are important friends where we are eating. We walk upstairs to the top floor of the house where there are views over the high street wall of the sports fields of Westminster School. My father's bedroom has a jade green colour on the walls and a matching silk-threaded bedspread. It is almost Japanese in style. He asks me to undress and walks into the bathroom next door to turn on the taps. Then he strips after drawing the curtains and turns to find me naked and waiting for his next instructions.

'Climb on the bed, boyzo,' he says, 'and I'll teach you some wrestling manoeuvres while we're waiting for the bath.'

He faces me as I prowl across the bed on my hands and knees. We grapple and sway in a kneeling position until he twists my arms behind my back. I go down like a sack of potatoes. I spring up again when he releases me and catch Dad round the waist, trying to bear down his heavy body. He twists and flips me over on my back. Then he tickles me until I am helpless with laughter. I roll over on my front and he drags me like a caveman to the side of the bed so my legs are hanging over the edge and touching the floor.

'Stay there a moment, Robbie, while I turn off the taps. The bath must be full by now. Don't move a muscle.'

Dad disappears inside the bathroom and I wait with my legs still dangling, wondering what's coming next. When he returns, Dad kneels behind me on the carpet and I feel watery hands on my backside. He is rubbing something into my anus. I guess it is a lotion of some kind and wonder why. Then he stops and straightens up.

'Hold on tight,' he murmurs.

I can feel him settling his legs between my thighs and leaning forward. He draws apart the opening between the cheeks of my bum. There is a slight pressure on the lips of my anus which I guess must be from his penis. Dad moves closer and the head pushes into the opening. It waits there for a moment and then pushes further. The lotion he has put on must be helping because the organ squeezes past the sphincter with some difficulty but not much. Dad pushes deeper until he has gone about three inches deep. Then he stops and mutters to himself.

He starts to move after another few moments, withdrawing and returning with regular, easy motions. This goes on for a minute or two until I hear him begin to groan loudly.

'Oh my God. Dear God!'

I can guess what's going to happen and it does - he begins to spurt. Immediately Dad grunts in distress and pulls out of me. His stuff shoots across my bum and my thighs as he moves his penis away. I guess he directs it after that at the carpet. He goes on muttering quietly but doesn't say anything more. We get up and throw ourselves in the waiting bath without a word more being spoken.

It feels odd chewing a half hour later on a Dover sole. The back has been opened up in the kitchen of Wheeler's and filled with creamy prawns. The waiters hover over me with napkins and keep refilling my water glass. My father is toasting me with a glass of white wine: a Niersteiner Spatlese possibly. Politicians and friends have queued up to say hello and they pat me on the head as they pass by. They chat about the likely quality of the skiing in the Alps this year. My Dover sole is dripping creamy butter off my fork onto the plate. Perhaps it's the dripping and the richness of the décor and the smell of the cigars…but suddenly it feels like my own white flesh has been opened up. That is what I am chewing on. There is some aching going on behind.

I push aside my plate and stand up giddily.

'What's the matter, boy?' Dad leans over the table, all concern.

'I think I'm going to be sick.'

'Why? What's the matter? Is anything wrong with your Dover sole?'

No, it's not that, I should reply. It's something else you know about…and tell him what it is, aloud. But of *course I don't. All I do is glance at Dad's face as if afraid he will be cross if I am sick right there at the table.*

'I'll go to the loo,' I say, hurrying down the passage between the tables.

I am feeling rather like I do in church when it is early morning and the candles are all lit. The oxygen is being sucked from the atmosphere by all the breathing and replaced with carbon dioxide. My head swims and I need to put my head between my legs otherwise I will faint. In the loo I throw up briefly and avoid looking in the pan in case I see something nasty there.

When we get home, Dad tucks me up in bed in the single room on the landing. I am relieved to be left alone. He kisses me on the cheek before he makes the usual sign of the cross on my forehead, kisses the spot there and goes out. I suppose that is meant to keep me protected through the night.

I have often pondered why my father chose that moment for his final act. I know the mechanics of what he did and the language that goes with it. I am not so naïve as that. I wish I'd had the courage to ask the question why during the last five years. But he would simply have avoided giving me a direct answer. So I have to imagine what it would be. Was it pure excitement before a skiing trip? Was he working up to the moment anyway? It had felt like that recently sometimes. Perhaps it was being away from Dorset that gave him the freedom to do what he wished.

ONE: Robbo, I simply lost my head. It WAS excitement – the thought of getting out of the stink of

London politics to the fresh air of the Swiss mountains. But more than that, it was the excitement of having you laid before me like an evening treat. The occasion went to my head. I hadn't planned it...well, not entirely. One thing led to another: the fighting and grappling of hands, the swaying on the bed, me flipping you on your back and then you turning over. All things contributed to the loss of control. I think there was a caveman instinct at work at that moment of dragging you to the edge of the bed. Also I have to say my London mattress is set at a convenient height. These factors are not excuses but simply explanations. The fact is I did wrong and I know that.

TWO: If you had groaned, dear boy – or even muttered a single sigh – I might have managed to stop myself. But you didn't; you lay still as marble as you always do. I was encouraged by that acquiescence. I thought you were OK with the final step. We had come close a few times and you hadn't made a sign of complaint. So I abandoned all caution. This isn't to blame you, boy. You didn't give me encouragement at any time, even if it was you who prowled across the bed so playfully.

THREE: I have to fall back on the old adage that I love you too much. Love should excuse all bedroom behaviour but it doesn't. I know what I feel for you is unacceptable in a father; I not only love but am IN LOVE with you. I feel the desire for you burning inside my chest. I'm not entirely sure where the feeling comes from but I need this fullness of experience with you. Your generosity is a factor that keeps me going in my working life. In the blackest moments when I am thinking of disaster, my thoughts turn to you and my burdens lighten. Your love permits me to perform as a politician, as a social reformer and as a man. But it is not acceptable; I recognise that.

I wrote these words on returning from Rome but I'm too tired and harrowed by the passage I have written to give any description of the day. So I'll leave that for tomorrow. I can hardly keep my eyes from closing and all I want to do is sleep.

Father Perceval and I went in together after breakfast on the crowded commuter train. The journey consisted of jostling shoulder to shoulder in the corridor with several hundred Italians standing eye to eye.

'What do you plan to do during the morning?' Father P asked as the train went skippety-skip along the track.

I shrugged. 'See the sights? The Colosseum, St Peter's?'

'How about visiting some museums of art? That would please your mother heartily. Make her feel you are doing something intellectual and artistic, not simply sight-seeing.'

I winced thinking how many of the Italians knew English and could guess how things stood between this dishevelled English boy and his Franciscan friar. Obviously Father P was acting as some kind of monitor in this situation. What they would never guess was that he had tried to monitor me at night. You don't immediately think of that when you look at priests and padres.

'I could go to a museum,' I offered.

'I have one in mind. It's on the Campidoglio,' Father Perceval said, staring at me with his appealing brown eyes. 'It's called the Capitoline and it's packed with sculpture on both sides of the square. After you've been there you could write a postcard to your mother, giving her full details of what you've seen. She'd be so pleased if you did that.'

I looked back at the monkish man, wondering why he was concerned that I should appear culturally switched-on. Had he promised Mum that he would reform me during the visit and turn me into an all-round, decent young man?

'How do I get to the Capitoline?' I asked sulkily.

'Simple. You come with me down the Via Nazionale from the station and keep on going after I turn right into Via Quattro Fontane. We'll pass the place where we are meeting for lunch, where the boys will be performing, so you can see where it is.'

I winced again, thinking of that audience of Romans and their flapping ears. What would the commuters make of the reference to performance? At the station when we arrived, I shuffled across the concourse in the wake of the padre, feeling like a juvenile on the way to reform school. Father P looked round constantly as if afraid I would run off. I hung a little behind. He kept glancing at me as if he would prefer to grab my hand and hold on tight. That would look even more bizarre to passers-by. We walked across the busy square and down the Via Nazionale, coming to a left hand bend where Father P pointed across the other side.

'That's the bar. We'll meet there at one o'clock and I'll introduce you to the boys. You'll like them a lot.'

How did he know what I would like?

'And the Capitoline?'

'Keep walking down the Nazionale until you get to the big piazza at the end with Vittorio Emanuele on his monument. You approach the Campidoglio on the other side up a long flight of steps. You can ask anyone for directions. Just ask for the Capitoline Museum if you can't find the way.'

I nodded and watched Father P skip across the busy road with his brown robe flying and his white tassels waving in the air. I set off down the street conscious of my ragged jeans and bare-toed sandals, wondering how soon I would be arrested by a policeman and searched for drugs. Could I please turn out my pockets? He wouldn't find anything except for a piece of chewing gum. Inside ten minutes I was climbing a long staircase to heaven wondering why no one had ever installed a lift. Soon after that I was standing in front of a bronze statue of Marcus Aurelius mounted on a horse. How different was that from the triumphalist Vittorio Emanuele in the square below? Wasn't that a good demonstration of what I was saying in my manuscript about power going to people's heads?

I entered the museum on one side of the square and pretty soon was facing the figure of the dying Gaul leaning on his arm. I was thinking how it would feel to be gashed like that with a sword, knowing that your life blood was running out. But wait a minute – there had been moments in my life when I had felt like that. One of them had been sitting on the edge of that London bed before the bath, staring down at the snail's trail running across my thigh.

Upstairs I passed a load of female figures and athletic youths handling the discus or standing in classic poses. I came in front of the small bronze of a naked boy sitting on a tree trunk, tending to a thorn in the sole of his foot. He was called Lo Spinario. I recognised myself in the lad. I suppose it was that damn fool pretence of innocence. You should not sit naked in a public place working at the sole of your foot unless you want to attract attention of the wrong kind. I hadn't learned that in childhood and neither had Lo Spinario. People were not going to stop and help you pull out a thorn: they would simply roll you over and attack your behind. I wanted to put out a hand to warn the boy of his danger but then I was sure a guard would tell me off for touching a statue. An annoying crowd of Japanese tourists were taking photographs of the foolish boy and I wanted to push them away. *Taking photos of this child is verboten. It's a pornographic offence. Go back to your hotel and destroy the film.*

With my feelings oddly jumbled, I shuffled out remembering Father Perceval's hints about postcards to my mother. I visited the shop and found plenty of photos of Lo Spinario and the Dying Gaul so I bought some to send to folk at home, composing messages in my head as I shuffled down the long flight of steps. 'Mum, do you think this boy looks like me at that age?' The trouble was she'd think I was

hinting at something. Was I blaming her for my naked troubles? I didn't give her a guilt trip by hinting
about pulling out thorns. Not much, I didn't.

I was sitting composing messages on a bench
in the little grassy park by the monument when I
became aware of a guy who had taken the same
bench as me. He looked like a student in his early
twenties. He was wearing a duffle coat against the
autumn chill and had a little goatee beard. He was
casting constant glances in my direction.

'You are German?' he asked politely in a
moment.

'No, English.'

'You are waiting for someone here?'

'No.' I wondered why he asked the question. I
guessed the answer when he spoke again.

'You want to see Rome?' the guy asked eagerly.
'I can arrange. I can show you everything inside the
city.'

I nodded politely.

'Here, I will show you exactly what I mean.'
The student dived inside the satchel beside him
and produced a pad of paper and a pencil. He started to draw. I saw a rectangle and then a door and
then the window of a room. 'This is my apartment.
It is only ten minutes' walk from here.'

'So?'

The student drew two figures on a bed with
little sticks popping up between their legs. 'You like
this idea?' he asked pleasantly. 'This can be you and
me. You want to do jig-i-jig?'

I stood up regretfully as if I didn't have time. I would but the trouble was the time.

'No, thanks. I have to meet someone round the corner soon.'

The meeting at the bar was in more than an hour's time so the explanation wasn't true. The student looked at me with pleading eyes. I shrugged politely and started to walk away. Luckily he didn't call after me.

I wandered down the Corso with all the busy fashion shops and stood for a long time on the bridge crossing the Tiber, thinking of that robust defender in the poem we had read about in prep school. He defended Rome against the barbarian hordes by standing alone barring the way across a narrow foot bridge. It might have happened more or less where I was standing now. I was a little bit like a guy defending a citadel: myself and my chastity. Except that citadel had already been taken. I wondered who would be the next to make an offer. Perhaps the Pope might if I went to see him. There must be something inside me these boy-busters could smell; some powerful scent of ambiguity. It must be noticeable to the senses otherwise they wouldn't hang about me. Wouldn't it be good if I had a long sword like the ancient Roman and could lay about me with the blade?

I wondered on towards St Peter's with that curving avenue of colonnades. I searched out with my eyes the balcony where the Pope stands when he is celebrating outdoor Mass. I guess I spotted the right place because the balcony had a red tapestry draped over it. I thought of tapping one of the colourful Swiss guards on the shoulder to ask to see His Eminence in person.

'I'd like a word with His Holiness if you please, my man.'

'What do you want to talk about?'

'I want to know why so many priests fall for boys, not only in the Catholic faith but the Protestant one. Is it because they see themselves as fathers and boys as their personal servants?'

I imagined the Swiss guard shuffling his stance and preparing to run me through with his halberd.

'I can't give you a good answer,' the guard might huff and puff. 'And neither could His Holiness. It's an impertinent question so be off out of here before I run you through.'

I arrived a little early at the café. There was no sign of the padre or the boys. The clientele consisted mainly of old men who sat in groups. I sat at a table near the back. I could see there was a raised platform with a drum kit and amplifiers already assembled. I guessed that was in readiness for our group. I hesitated whether to order a pizza as I was hungry or if that would be considered rude by Father P when he arrived. Also there was the consideration of payment. What happened if he failed to show and I was left with the bill? I might be washing dishes for the rest of the day. My Mum had not left me much in the way of cash, trusting more to the padre's pocket than to mine. When the bartender asked if I wanted a drink, I ordered beer. I explained in halting English that I was meeting an English priest who was expected with a bunch of orphan boys.

'*Ah, sei con il gruppo!*' the man exclaimed.

'*Si, si.*'

'*Allora va bene! Una birra.*'

At half past one Father Perceval and his merry troupe arrived, dragging their music cases with them. I wished the floor would open up and swallow me as they were all about fourteen. One of them had a guitar in a zip-up bag and another a hard case with a saxophone. A third had an accordion and the last had nothing. He was the babe of the group who was at least a year younger than the others. He hopped up quickly behind the drum kit to practice once he had shaken my hand: round-faced, pink-lipped and cute.

'Aren't they terrific?' Father P asked me breathlessly as the boys started rehearsing for their first song. 'Sorry we're a little late. There was some delay at the orphanage. That is Niccolo who is lead singer and guitarist.' He was pointing at the tallest boy behind the microphone. 'That is Pietro on saxophone and Michele on the accordion. Ludovico is the youngest one on drums.'

I watched them as they played, standing just a couple of yards away. The one I was looking at was the drummer. He had bright apple cheeks. He was a bit like Lo Spinario with that parting down the middle of his curly hair. I was getting that odd jumpy feeling in the pit of my tummy, the same as when I wanted to reach out and touch the statue's knee. It was something to do with innocence being snatched away; the longing to give warning. It felt like my responsibility to do so. *Take care of yourself. Don't make yourself a target. Otherwise you're going to get screwed like me.*

The school chaplain has let it be known that he is available for private chats with boys who have troubled souls. One day during Easter term I detain him at the end of choir practice. He is a red-faced man with polished shoes that you can practically see your face in and a receding hairline.

'Sir, may I see you for a few minutes?'

'What, during break?'

'If that's OK with you.'

He gives me a long-suffering glance as he is probably thinking of his coffee and the ginger biscuits that are reserved for staff in the masters' common room.

'All right, Monty. Will ten minutes be enough?'

Will ten hours or days or weeks?

'Yes, sir. That will do just fine.'

The chaplain ushers me into a small flat adjoining the church and a sofa in the sitting-room. The cushions on the armchairs have been stitched with needlepoint. I can imagine the ladies in his last parish agitating for months over the designs and going to endless tea parties to discuss the topic.

'What is it, boy?' he asks as he flops down.

'There's something I need to sort out at home going on between me and Dad,' I say painfully.

The parson's wiry eyebrows shiver and lift like butterflies.

'You don't get on well? You can't see eye to eye?'

'No, sir. The opposite. Dad's very close to me; especially so. He finds it hard to leave me alone. He writes me letters at school often.'

The clergyman blinks at me.

'So what are you complaining about?'

'I'm not quite complaining. It's a lot for me to handle, sir. I don't think it's fair on everyone else in the family.'

I have twisted the story to avoid the point which is staring at me like a flashing beacon. The vicar hiccups and gives a short grunt to clear the air. He leans forward and pats me on the knee, then sets to polishing it with his hand like a mirror.

'Dear boy, you are lucky to have such a problem. Most boys are given too little time by their fathers. If yours loves you head and shoulders above the rest, you should be celebrating the fact.'

'I am, sir. But as I say it's a bit too much…'

I am not explaining this well. How can I? It's beyond the normal run of words. I look at the man's grinning face and he continues to rub my knee. What makes all clergymen do that? A boy's knee is obviously in need of a constant rub like a brass plate in church otherwise it gets mucky.

'Your father's a top politician, is he not, Monty? An important man. He cares for you above all. You should be pleased. That's something to cherish.'

I sigh at the mistaken direction of our chat.

'I do, sir. But shouldn't he be looking more in other directions?'

The chaplain considers my face a moment.

'You mean cherishing your brother and sisters more?'

'Oh no, sir! Not too much of that!' The man has conjured up an image that is an appalling thought.

'You seem confused.' The chaplain stands. 'I need to take my tea break. Just remember, Monty. Boys owe their fathers all the world.'

'Yes, sir. I know that.'

How should I have gone about making a proper confession of my father's sins and my part in his wrong-doing? I had tried with the vicar and failed because I didn't state my case. I had tried exploring the subject with a friend but Walter didn't catch my drift. What I needed to do was to speak to my mother and put her in the picture. But I couldn't face her distress nor my feelings of shame. Would she have believed me anyway? Mum was getting on well with my father by then. They were exchanging frequent letters and calls. *My dear Rosemary…my dear Hinch…Can't we find a time to see each other?* I could hear them gurgling down the telephone. My mother was also drinking a lot most nights. Was I going to march into her sitting room and tell her my Dad was interfering with me when she might not even understand what I was saying? Like hell I would.

So who am I interviewing today about this stage of events? It was a bit like waiting in an anteroom to hell. Someone must reveal this burning secret before too long or I should be damned eternally and turned into a regular Ganymede prepared to serve his nectar to the Gods.

ONE: (Mum) Certainly you should have come to me, not to some silly vicar. If you had told me exactly what was happening, I would have believed you totally. Your imagination was known as lively but not to that extent. I would have put a stop to all contact. Do you think I would have allowed you to continue visiting him? I would not have dismissed you and poured myself another whisky, if that's your fear. The news would have had the opposite effect. I would have led a crusade against your father and put him in prison.

Oh yes, Mum – are you sure?

TWO: (Dad) You needed and were doing what most boys of your age learn at that age: to button your lips. Isn't that what they teach you at school? The first requirement in life is to go through all ordeal without complaint. Take what life dishes out to you. That's what you learn in the army. Besides, you've already said that you were not physically damaged. My actions might have been misguided but they were done only out of excessive love. The story was not the business of others. If you had spread the word, it would have spelled the end of politics for me and probably the end of my status as a free man.

THREE: (Kate) We all loved our father and felt sorry for him, alone without Mum. It would have killed the family if you had spoken to anyone. You were right to hold back and wait for his acts to stop. Surely they would have ended naturally. Dad wasn't a wild beast, just a lonely person. He went too far a few times, yes he did...OK, much too far...and it's horrible what he did. But don't you think you played a part?

'So what did you make of the boys in Rome?' Father Perceval asked before he left for town this morning.

I squirmed over the breakfast cereals.

'Honestly? They were pretty good rubbish, to be frank.'

'How can you say that? The crowd in the café seemed pleased as Punch.'

I gave him one of my hang-dog expressions that don't commit me to further comment. I had given my opinion: the performance was lousy and off-key. The Beatles would have sued for defamation of their material. The singer couldn't seem to lift his voice to the higher notes and Ludovico bashing at the drums seemed keener to break the membrane than to mark the rhythm. Anyway I didn't want to encourage the padre with praise of the band in case he came up with some mad scheme to involve us more closely. Probably that was what he had in mind already. He sniffed and looked at me in that keen way of his. I knew those watery brown eyes were up to something fishy.

'What do you think of having the boys over for a performance here?' he asked as if he was guessing what I was thinking.

'HERE? What, you mean in the castle?'

'Why not?'

'Over my dead body,' I yelled at him.

'What makes you so cross about that idea?' Father P walked round me a couple of times in a considering way. 'They can come for a weekend and give a concert in the hall for local people. There's space enough to put in chairs.'

I shut my eyes, hoping the vision would go away: a band of teenage ragamuffins slaughtering the works of the Beatles, of Bob Dylan and seaside crooners like Celentano. I also didn't wish to see the apple-cheeked lad who reminded me of Lo Spinario – particularly as he had got those churning feelings going inside my tummy.

'You bring that group to the castle,' I said snappily, 'and I'm going out the back door when you arrive.'

Father P looked at me steadily as though I was proving what a fallen angel I was. It was his job to restore me to my perch.

'You're being unreasonable,' he said. 'Talking of running away when you should be holding firm, Robert. You've already done a bolter once in the last few weeks. That's enough.'

'Fuck off!' I may have murmured under my breath, after which he didn't speak to me for the rest of the evening.

It's the Easter holidays and I am back at my father's house. He has returned to using his large white handkerchief although clumsily and that conveys the message to me that what happened between us before the skiing holiday was overstretching the mark in his view. We are back to the steady piston action between the cheeks and hot kisses on the neck. I have perfected an art that he enjoys when we are finished. I walk naked to the fire-place, turn and launch myself at the bed in a series of missile strikes. There may be something Freudian in this, seeing as I narrowly miss his head when I crash down. Dad has given names to each type of rocket: there's the slow moving Russian sputnik and a low scorcher that comes in from the USA. The British model is somewhere in between and twists in mid-air so it lands on one side.

My sisters are at the house for Easter and my brother is as well. There is a heap of guests including a Cabinet minister. A shoot takes place in the deepest woods. I take part with a .410 shotgun that my father has bought me at Christmas. I wound a rabbit and Dad orders me to kill it by wringing its neck. I don't know how to do this and don't feel capable of murder. Luckily one of the hunters steps forward to do the job with a quick flick of the wrist and I imagine the rabbit in his hands as a German night watchman during the war.

Dad wants me to shoot at a young deer. I should refuse his command but don't. I look at the blood running down the deer's flank – luckily I have caught it in the chest – and my tears of sympathy flow. I am wondering when I am going to stop doing whatever my Dad desires whenever he asks for it.

One evening my mother calls on the telephone while I am taking my usual bath with my father. We have moved down the corridor to the bathroom on the south side so as to give space for guests. At least that's my Dad's explanation for finding a remote place. My sister Julia comes looking for me and calls my name. Dad answers, motioning with a finger to his lips for me to keep silent.

'What is it, Julia?'

'I'm looking for Robert.'

Ignoring Dad's instruction to be quiet, I answer from the bath where I am sitting in my usual place between his thighs.

'I'm here. What do you want?'

'It's Mum on the phone. She wants to speak to you.'

'Tell her I'm coming in a moment.'

As I stand to climb out, my father looks at me, upset with what I've said. What's wrong with it? My sister's voice comes through the door, sounding a trifle disgusted.

'Are you sharing a bath with Dad in there? At your age? How weird is that? Yuck!'

'Go away,' Dad shouts angrily at Julia.

He looks at me accusingly as I dry myself but says nothing more. Wrapped in my towel, I rush for the nearest phone.

'Hi, Mum.'

She asks about the Easter holidays at my father's house, the people at the dinner parties and the shoot. I give her the news standing there dripping in my towel. I see my sisters are watching me and whispering together but I think nothing of what they might be saying.

At dinner time, my food is brought up as usual by the housekeeper while I am in bed reading Hans Christian Andersen's fairy tales. Around nine o'clock when I have just switched off the light, the door of my room opens and my sisters appear in their rustling gowns. Kate puts on the main light and I rub my eyes as she and Julia walk over in excitement and sit down on my bed.

'What do you want?' I ask sleepily.

'To hear more about what you were doing, sharing a bath with Dad before dinner.'

'We've always done that,' I say.

'Since when?' Kate asks, cuddling up.

'Since a long time ago. At least the last three years.'

'It can't be so,' says Julia. 'We would have known it.'

'It's true, I promise you.'

My two sisters exchange glances full of meaning.

'You mean you actually get inside the tub together?'

'Sure. What's wrong with that?'

'What happens next?'

'We wash ourselves. Mainly Dad washes me.'

More exchange of glances.

'You mean he washes you all over, including your willy and your bum?'

'Yes. Why not?'

I feel a trickle of ice sliding down my backbone. I always knew there was something wrong with sharing baths even until I was eleven.

'It's not normal,' Kate says. 'Not at your age.'

I open and close my mouth but cannot speak. How young or old do you have to be for a shared bath?

Eventually the two go away and let me sleep. The resting is not easy and I toss and turn all night. I don't believe this is going to be the end of the enquiry and it isn't.

I have to wonder hard whether God or one of his angels had a hand in this discovery. The only way to know is to ask God and so I will. God, did YOU put the idea in Mum's head to call at a time when you knew I would be in the bath with Dad? Did YOU fix it so that Julia would come along the corridor to look for me and find us in the bath together? Was this what you might call a rescue mission on my behalf?

ONE: (God speaking) Yes, I have to say this was an idea we Immortals did discuss in our regular business meeting on that day. We had been following your progress for quite some time, as we do with all those in your position. Unfortunately we don't have the power to intervene directly. We are if you like similar to ghosts who have no physical presence; we can only influence through whispering. Your mother called you because she was feeling like doing so. You might say that an angel whispered in her ear to suggest it but I couldn't possibly comment on that.

TWO: (still God) I suppose you do remember the message you sent up years earlier? I think it was after singing *Lead me, Lord* in chapel and then praying next to your father to forgive your sins. We do listen out for messages, you know; no matter how many of them there are. They are like calls for help sent in a bottle with a cork. Unfortunately as I say, there is nothing we can do physically but we can plant thoughts in people's minds…and that's what happened in this case.

THREE: (still God) Here's a strange thing. Your father also sent us a message, immediately after what happened in London. He begged us to help him peg back what he was doing. He didn't want more of that to happen to his son. We pigeon-holed the messages and came up finally with the decision to whisper in your mother's ear. Now do you understand the process? I am afraid it is against our rules for me to be precise.

I got up from my desk in the castle just now and went to make myself a mug of coffee. I was shivering, not out of cold though the place was DAMP, but because of these question marks in the back of my mind. Was God really involved or was He and the angels merely a figment of my imagination, which I was wasting my time giving voice to? Maybe out there behind the stars there was NOTHING spiritual and when I was dead there would be NOTHING to saving me rotting in the earth; the idea of spiritual influence was wholly WRONG.

I brought back the mug and stood staring at the valley for a few minutes. It wasn't raining but wasn't sunny either. The afternoon sky was heavy with dark puffy clouds sweeping deep shadows across the landscape. I was mindful of the bucket and rags waiting to be applied to the walls of the room upstairs. If the boys came by, that was where they would be sleeping and the redecorations needed finishing beforehand. But I had no heart for them.

I was thinking of Father Perceval's face when he came home and asked for more details of how I had spent my day. I had to tell him sooner or later about my writing. Why delay? I couldn't carry the burden of the past forever on my own. It wasn't fair. It wasn't surprising I was incapable of washing down walls when half of me wanted to bolt by jumping out of a window. If I revealed the writing, at least Father P would partly understand what was going on in my mind.

I'm home in London for three days before return-ing to school for the summer term. The first evening my mother and sisters are unusually quiet. I am unsure if the conversation of the night-time has been forgotten. We play cards in the sitting-room and my mother puts on Greek music as she is going through a language phase and hoping to visit the country soon with her girlfriend. There is a curious absence of talk about my father's house and doings. We talk more about my mother's lat-est exploits and parties she has been to; plans for the next holidays. I turn in early, believing that shopping for school clothes will be the main focus of next day as my bones seem to be putting on a spurt and I am shoot-ing up like Jack and the beanstalk.

At breakfast I am alone. Mum's Irish housekeeper serves me a larger plate of bacon and eggs than usual as if I need to be well fortified today.

'Eat that up,' she urges. 'You're going to need it.'

'For what?'

She won't say.

The doorbell rings and I think this is the postman. Instead it is our family doctor; a curious visit at such an hour. Is someone unwell? He refuses breakfast but accepts a large cup of black coffee from the housekeeper.

'Is your mother down?'

'No, not yet. Is everything OK?'

'Oh yes.' The doctor raises his shaggy eyebrows to me. 'We'll wait.'

I continue eating my bacon and eggs, wondering whether it is impolite to ask WHY the doctor is visiting us. A skittering of nerves is pulling at my tummy muscles. I hear the tread on the stairs of my mother's steps. The weight is heavier than my sisters' and the steps creak. Mum greets the doctor and kisses my forehead, then weighs a hand heavily on my shoulder. I glance up at her troubled expression.

'What's wrong?'

'Nothing. When you've finished, come into the sitting-room, Robbie.'

My mother beckons the doctor to follow her. I finish loading my plate into the dumb waiter so it is ready to descend into the kitchen. I knock at the sitting-room door.

'Come in.'

Mum and the doctor are sitting in two wing-backed arm chairs with corduroy covers on either side of the fire-place, facing the green velvet sofa. Mum makes a gesture for me to sit down. At once alarm bells start ringing in my head like school bells calling assembly. My sisters have betrayed me to the high priests of the family and not even waited around to see me questioned. I sit trembling, waiting for the inquisition to begin. There are small birds hopping about on the spring cherry tree outside the window. I wish I could be there with them and not sitting on the green sofa.

'We've been told about an odd conversation you had with your sisters one or two evenings ago,' the doctor begins in a kindly voice. 'Perhaps you can help us to make sense of it, Robert.'

Perhaps I can and perhaps I can't, I am thinking. Perhaps I shouldn't. Perhaps to say anything is a terrible idea.

'This bath business,' my mother explains, looking stricken.

Perhaps ignorance is my best defence. Perhaps I could just say it was a single bath I took with him, no more – not one repeated over several years.

'Julia and Kate say you told them you had been sharing a bath with your father for at least three years: that he gets in with you every evening and washes you all over.'

So Mum already knows about the number of baths. I nod my head. What else can I do? It's too late to pretend a single event.

'Your Dad bathes all your body with his hands?' checks my mother. 'Not using a sponge or hand towel.'

'No – with his hands.'

'Including your penis and your bottom?' checks the doctor.

I nod and note the specific references to parts.

'With you standing up or kneeling?' the question comes.

'Kneeling.'

'Away from him or facing your father?'

'Both.'

'For how long does he wash your private parts?' asks the doctor.

'I don't know. Two or three minutes, maybe.'

'Does he clean inside the foreskin of your penis?'

'Yes.'

'How does he wash your bottom? I mean, does he use his fingers to clean inside?'

'No!' I say with emphasis.

'Does he...?' My mother leans forward. 'Does Dad's body change at all while he is doing this?'

I don't understand what she means.

'I mean...to be blunt, Robbie, does his penis stand up at any time to show he is excited?'

'No,' I say, red-faced.

I stare at my mother. Whatever might she ask next? I drag my eyes away and watch those little birds chatting in the cherry tree. I am envying them whatever it is they are talking about.

'OK, let's turn to what happens between the two of you during the rest of the day,' the doctor suggests, changing direction like a practised barrister. 'Do you see your father on your own at any other time?'

I glance back at the scholarly face with the horn-rim spectacles. The doctor's face is somewhat like that of Punch from an old cartoon, with a bulbous nose and thrusting jaw.

'Yes. Dad reads me a story every day before break-fast,' I say. I can't exactly lie. Anyone can ask the house-keeper for this information.

'What time is that?' my mother asks.

'About seven-thirty.'

'How long does that go on?'

'About an hour or so.'

'Do you snuggle up together in his bed?'

I nod.

'Is anyone else ever there with you to see what's going on?'

I shake my head.

'What else happens beside the story?' the doctor asks. 'That's a long time to read. You talk, you play...?'

'We listen to the radio,' I say.

'And what else?'

'Josie comes in with a tray of tea and orange juice at eight o'clock.'

The doctor and Mum exchange glances. 'So Josie sees you there with him every day?'

'Yes,' I say happily as if I've won a round. 'She even brings me my own glass of orange juice.'

'What happens once she's gone?' the doctor persists gently.

'Nothing.' I think the reply is not full enough and search around for something innocuous to add. 'I do some dives on the bed from across the room, like missile launches.'

'What about before you get out of bed?' he probes. 'Does your father ever tickle you...or run his hands over you at any time?'

I wobble, thinking this area is getting dodgy. But I don't want to lie directly. I must not.

'Sometimes.'

'Does he feel your muscles, explore your body and see how it's shaping up?'

I consider that. Wouldn't it be a normal thing to say yes?

'Sometimes.'

I watch the doctor framing his next question carefully.

'Are there also times when your father takes off your pyjamas to explore your body more thoroughly?'

I am aware how dangerous my answer to this question is. But it's a direct one. How do I say no without lying? Dad does this every day and takes huge pleasure in it.

'Sometimes,' I say again.

I am aware of my mother drawing in her breath.

'Does he then – in the course of that exploration – touch you on your penis or your bottom?'

What can I say? I look towards the birds outside the window for help. Would one of them answer for me? Say tweet-tweet.

'You must answer Dr Scott,' directs Mum.

'Yes, sometimes he does.'

'What do you do then?' the doctor asks.

My answer is a whisper. 'I pretend to go to sleep.'

'So it goes on then for some time? This touching of you.'

I nod.

'What is your Dad doing exactly at this time? Is he touching you with his hands only or with any other part of his body?'

'Other parts as well,' I say.

I am aware that Mum and the doctor are muttering together though my eyes are half closed to shut out the light.

'Which parts?'

'All of them.'

'You mean his penis too?' my mother asks in a half sob.

I nod my head. And his mouth, I am thinking. I am not looking at her. She doesn't exist if I keep my eyes tight closed.

'Does he use his mouth also?' asks the doctor.

'Yes,' I mumble.

'What did you say?'

'Yes, he does.'

I can hear my mother begin to sob.

'Oh Robbie! How is this possible? Are you sure that's true?'

I can't go on with this enquiry. It has to stop. But how do I bring it to an end? If I run for the door, my Mum and the doctor will simply come after me and haul me back.

'Let me continue with the questions,' Dr Scott suggests gently. 'What exactly does your father do with his penis?'

'You can't ask Robert that!' my Mum explodes.

'I have to.'

The doctor leans forward towards me. 'Robert, has your father ever put his penis inside your body?'

'Once,' I say.

'ONCE!' my mother shrieks.

'Mostly he does it on a handkerchief,' I add as if that makes it better.

'ON A HANDKERCHIEF!'

At that point I start to cry. Tears spring to my eyes and start to flow down my cheeks no matter how hard I keep my eyelids closed. I am aware of my Mum yelling more questions. She is sobbing like I am and the doctor *is asking her to calm down. It is my cue to disappear and so I get up from the sofa with my eyes pouring and I rush for the door headlong.*

You have to feel some sympathy for Mum. It isn't ever going to be easy to hear that your husband has interfered sexually with your child; in fact, I'd have to guess that it's a killer blow. Really it needs a professional to ask the questions, not a mother and not even a family doctor; someone trained in the art of careful questioning of children. What Mum and the doctor did in that meeting was about the worst thing possible. I had to fill in all the details later about the use of the penis and the mouth, the method of riding up and down, the white handkerchief and everything else that took place. At the end of the morning I was left feeling so trashed that if a window had been left open and myself unattended, I would have surely gone through it. Mum stationed my sisters beside me to play endless games. I think it was Monopoly that went on and on for hours as soon as I could be persuaded to join in. Shopping for clothes was postponed until the final day before I went back to school. In the end Kate came with me and not Mum who pleaded sickness.

All the time I was imagining what Mum was doing now: having meetings, consulting lawyers and policemen. Would more people be waiting to interview me when I got back home? Perhaps Mum would be phoning my father and there would be an unholy scene going on with screams and curses and threats hurled down the telephone. I would be prevented from ever seeing the man again except behind prison bars. Next thing I knew, my Dad would be in the dock at the Old Bailey and I would be in the witness box with the prosecution urging me to tell all the details about his handkerchief.

But no – when I got home that last day, all was quiet. We had a family dinner round the table with my brother and sisters present and not a word was spoken about Dad. It was all about what was happening at school and my brother's plans to take a year off before starting university: where exactly he would go in the Far East and Africa. Next day I took the usual train from Paddington, packed with other boys in their grey school uniforms. No question of putting it off for a few days. *Hello, Parry. Hello, Mortimer.* Shining faces talking about their Easter holidays in the Caribbean. Nothing about Dads and beds and bottoms plumped up on pillows. No legal questions and no policemen in sight.

So who gets the questions in this chapter? Everybody. Clearly there were big discussions going on to which I was not invited. The conclusion was, get Robert off to school and out of the way while we work out the programme of events. He can take the suspense and make what he likes of it. There's no point in sharing our dilemmas and making the boy hysterical.

ONE: (Mum) We weren't even certain that what you were telling us was the truth. It needed to

108

be verified in some independent way. John needed to go down to Dorset to confront your father and get some facts. Josie had to be interviewed about what she knew. It needed to be seen if any evidence could be found. The trouble was that what you told us didn't square with anything we knew about your father. It was known there were special friends in his life and it's true I had accused him a few times of homosexuality. He had accused me of the same so there was a stand-off over that. But buggery of his own son! That takes a lot to believe. Even then if we did believe you, what to do about the appalling fact was going to take an awful lot of thinking and talking.

TWO: (John) You remember that quality in you of exaggeration that you always had? I thought we had a classic case of that. I thought that what Dad actually did were minor misdemeanours and you had blown them out of all proportion. It was your imagination going over strong, that was what. So we had to tread carefully. It wouldn't make sense to put my father in the dock over trivialities. Where would that have left you, but exposed to the world as a junior fantasist?

THREE: (Julia) I was feeling awful because it was me who found you together in the bath and started the ball rolling. I wanted the investigation to stop right there. It was like a nightmare growing bigger all the time. I wanted to go back to school and forget all about it. I was having a hard enough time myself adjusting to puberty and getting on with exams and relationships. I didn't want to be the girl who cried *Woof, woof!* like I used to do through that bedroom pipe.

Father Perceval told me this evening that the fact I hadn't completed washing down the walls upstairs meant he was going to have to change his plans.

'I'm going to stay here with you until we have finished the room together,' he told me. 'There'll be no excuses tomorrow. Two hours' work should do it if we start early. Then I can go to work. You can do whatever it is you like during the day. In the evening I will bring home a special dinner and we will eat it with a fine bottle of Chianti. We will light a fire and tell stories about our lives and get drunk on grappa. What do you say to that?'

I gave a gruff assent.

'Then you can start painting properly next day. At least promise me to do two hours daily and that's enough. OK?'

I nodded without saying anything and retired early to my bed.

It's weird being at prep school and waiting every day for a summons to the headmaster's office. I am waiting to hear that my Dad has been arrested and a date has been set for a trial. It's also weird going about your daily life, rehearsing with the choir and trying to follow algebraic equations in class, expecting at any moment to be called for an interview with the police. Where are the inspectors with their notebooks and sharp pencils? I might also wonder why the morning newspapers keep arriving – especially the Sundays – and there's no story about my father and me, showing my butter-wouldn't-melt-in-the-mouth face hugging him tight.

The days go by and no such thing occurs. Instead I receive a short letter from Kate, filling me in on events before she left for school. Apparently my Mum sent my Dad a telegram on the day I returned to Oxford, quoting a passage from the New Testament: St Matthew Chapter 18, verse 6 to be exact. 'WHOSO – SHALL – OFFEND – ONE – OF –THESE – LITTLE – ONES – WHICH – BELIEVE – IN – ME, – IT – WERE – BETTER – FOR - HIM - THAT – A – MILLSTONE – WERE – HANGED - ABOUT – HIS – NECK – AND – THAT – HE – WERE - DROWNED – IN – THE – DEPTH – OF – THE – SEA.'

My sister adds in her letter that my Mum received a telegram again the next day quoting the New Testament back: this time St. Mathew Chapter 7, verse 3. 'WHY – BEHOLDEST – THOU – THE - MOTE – THAT – IS – IN – THY - BROTHER'S – EYE - BUT – CONSIDEREST – NOT – THE – BEAM – THAT – IS – IN – THINE – OWN – EYE?'

This has my heart beating fast. What beam are we talking about? My Mum's preference for women, I take it. OK, that's a beam for me personally but one that a lot of other boys share; it sometimes comes with the deal of changing partners. What my sister Kate doesn't say – perhaps she doesn't know – is where the machinery of justice is churning away or perhaps grinding to a halt. Have writs been issued against my father? Will he be arrested and put on trial? What have the police advised? Why have I not been told by anybody what is going on? It's only my sorry arse and future that's at stake here. It would be nice to know when the guillotine is going to descend on my father's head.

Will my Dad be attending to business meanwhile, turning up to make speeches in the House of Commons? Or is he already rotting in some deep dungeon of the Tower of London? Will an article appear in The Daily Express that exposes everything: even the jade colour of Dad's bedroom wall and the type of silk handkerchief he prefers to use?

More days go by without news. I am longing to phone home to hear what is happening. Such a request has to be funnelled through the headmaster so I need to whip up the courage to speak to the cadaverous man.

'Please, sir. I am waiting to hear whether my Dad has been arrested for incest and buggery. May I phone home?' I don't think so.

I eye the HM across the floor in the school hall, sitting among his staff at the high table: tall and reedy, looking ready for the grave. How will I actually phrase the question: by telling him I think my mother is sick? What happens instead is that I receive a message next day in the classroom to visit the headmaster's study urgently.

'Robert, you have to go right away. There's news from home.'

This is it: the update I have been waiting for. I knock on the shiny black door and a voice summons me to enter. I stand to attention inside with my arms behind my back as you would do at ease on a parade ground. The headmaster raises his hangdog eyes from his desk blotter and clears his throat.

'Ah, Robert. Sit down, my boy. I'm afraid there is bad news.'

I perch on the armchair over which I have previously been caned.

'Quite serious news from your family. Your sister Julia has been taken ill. She has been flown to hospital by helicopter and is now in a critical condition: a coma, in fact.'

What? How can this be?

'The doctors suspect the cause may be meningitis. I'm afraid it's not known at the moment whether your sister will live or die.'

My thoughts have been thrown into a sudden whirlpool. Julia is the one who discovered Dad and my-

self in the bath. It was she who whispered the news to Kate and later on my Mum. Now Julia has been attacked by a mysterious disease and may die. Is this heavenly retribution — a punishment for telling about me and Dad?

'The school will pray for your sister's recovery,' the headmaster says. 'Every morning in chapel while Julia is in intensive care. I have already given instructions. Have you any questions from your side? Otherwise you may return to your class, Robert.'

Have I any questions? Sure, I have tons. Chiefly they are spiritual ones addressed to God. I am not sure how the HM can help with those. Is this what God means by changing people's feelings? Has some angel administered a voodoo punishment of some kind to my sister? From being normal a few days ago, she is now in a coma — how often does that happen in real life? It isn't natural. God must be on the side of punishment. That means He is on the same side as the sinners: me and Dad.

I call home and am given more details. Julia is in a deep coma and they are waiting for her to come round or die. No one can do anything to help. I don't ask Mum why this has happened. How can I ask her which side the angels are on? A letter comes next day from my father in unusually spidery handwriting. It seems his poodle bit my sister at some point during the holidays. He is worried that the dog's bite might have been infectious and caused her illness. Like rabies? No, I doubt that, though I am not a medical expert. The truth is he caused her illness by telling her roughly to leave the bathroom and tempting her to gossip. The letter only gives me more reason to believe the Godly intervention. I also note there is nothing in Dad's letter about us or the police.

Every day in chapel, the vicar adds Julia to his list of prayers.

'We pray for young Julia Montagu, sister of Robert, who is lying in hospital in a coma. We pray for her complete recovery.'

Boys eye me from the pews through their blinkered fingers, half sympathetic and half hoping I will respond with some dramatic performance. If I burst into tears and weep on the altar cloth, that will give them something to talk about for the rest of the day – better than a film, really. I have a leaden heart because of my own guilt feelings. Ghostly forces are siding with my father and punishing my sister. There seems little doubt they will soon turn on myself. After all who was it who broke down and told the truth during a meeting with his mother?

Maybe I should write Mum a note saying that everything I told her and the doctor was a lie. That way my sister will be released from her punishment by the ghostly forces and they may even spare me. There'll be no meeting with the police and no story in the newspapers. I will sit down this evening during prep and write the message.

But when it comes to the deed, I cannot write. My pen won't handle the deceit. Besides I don't believe it will make a difference to my sister's health. If I recant like those mediaeval monks before they died at the stake, *all I am doing is condoning a huge sin. What I have said so far is not a lie: none of it is. If anything it is a minimization of the truth. There may have been more times when I was buggered than the once and I have glossed over the details, unwilling to remember.*

A day comes two weeks later when I am called to the headmaster's study for a second time. Intense glances from other boys follow me down the passage to the HM's study. People squeeze my arm and whisper me good luck as if I am on my way to the gallows.

The man looks up with a bright smile – as much as he is capable of one.

'Your sister Julia has woken from her coma, boy. I've just had the news from your mother. She is paralysed down one side but it looks like Julia is going to survive.'

Thank God, she has been reprieved by Heaven. So her whistle-blowing was not a crime.

I have a number of questions today, addressed to Julia. What exactly does she think caused her illness back then? Does she buy the doctors' story about meningitis brought on by infected water in the Isle of Wight or does she believe it was my father's poodle? Was it dark forces from above or below that weaved a spell around her for gossiping?

ONE: (Julia) My illness had nothing to do with dark forces or the saliva from Dad's dog. Probably it was a simple bug I picked up somewhere. I nearly died but was saved by brilliant nursing. It had nothing to do with God's wishes. I was back at school

116

before the end of term, dragging a leg and spending most of my time in a wheelchair but reasonably alive.

TWO: You mustn't believe all these fantasies about fate and God and the devil, brother dearest. These are all devices in your mind which is still suffering with shame and guilt over what happened with Dad. Get over your feelings and move on, that's my advice. That's what I am trying to do with my paralysis. YOU don't have scars from an emergency tracheotomy in your throat. YOU don't have to drag a leg or have someone spoon food into your mouth. Be grateful for small mercies. Deal with your mental scars yourself. Others are not going to be much help to you; they never are.

THREE: Don't worry about what will happen with Dad. Time will tell. You'll be told what to expect in the holidays. The answer may not be black and white. People have to think about the future and what's best for everyone. There are so many issues at stake, not just justice over you. My little brother is just a small cog in a big machine. Wait and see what happens, little cog.

We had that hearty dinner that Perceval promised yesterday and it was fun getting drunk in front of a roaring fire. He asked me PLEASE to start the painting tomorrow and I promised I would as we had finished the walls during the morning.

He asked me in front of the fire what it was that I was doing all day that was so captivating that

I was neglecting work. I finally decided to own up and confessed that I was busy writing.

'Writing what, exactly?' he pondered.

'The story of my life – at least one miserable section of it.'

Father P thought for a long moment and then wagged a finger in front of my eyes.

'You mean you're writing about the relationship with your Dad.'

I nodded. That was about the size of it. After all there wasn't much else interesting about my life. The padre had heard all about the business during the summer term when we first met. He was grinning at me and nodding wisely at his guesswork.

'That's about right,' I said.

'Can I read the work?' he asked then, as I knew he would. 'As much as you've got so far?'

By then the man had consumed about six glasses of Chianti so his reading skills might have left something to be desired, to say nothing of his sympathies.

'No, you can't,' I told him bluntly. 'It's private and for me alone.'

'Can't we at least discuss what you have written?'

I shrugged. What was the point in that? Was Father Perceval going to correct my English and provide answers to my questions? He was outside the family window, so to speak. All he could do was pretend to know the answers, like a stranger. There was also the fact that he had tried to jump on me that first night; that somewhat weakened his position as a judge. More than that, it showed that he actually belonged in the ranks of the wicked like my father. What kind of bias would that give his opinion?

'I'll think about it,' I said. What I was thinking was, maybe as a predator himself Father Perceval could give me useful insights.

May turns into June and I am scheduled to play cricket in a match on a Saturday afternoon. A message comes from the sports master that my father will be coming to visit shortly after lunch. I have permission to join the match once we have finished our meeting.

I can guess why Dad is coming, of course. He is coming to apologize for the last five years. He will tell me he is going away for a year or two to spend some time in contemplation – in gaol, in other words. Or perhaps in a Buddhist monastery. After that our shared holidays may resume again under strict conditions. My visits to his room will cease and there will be no more shared baths or passionate cuddles. I will receive some explanation of how everything happened: what pressures built up in my Dad that he felt he must expend on me. I expect the confession will go on so long that I will miss the cricket match entirely. But no matter: this is more important than trying to beat the Dragon batsmen.

I watch his Bentley turn into the school yard and park. I am dressed in whites ready for the game. Dad gets out in a blue suit as if he is going to a wedding. I am wondering how to greet him: with an unguarded hug and kisses on both cheeks or by shaking Dad's hand as if he is an unknown visitor?

In the end I give a combination of a hug and a handshake, which confuses him as much as me.

Dad asks where we might go to be private and I lead him to a bench at the edge of the cricket field where we can watch the players setting up. There is a large spreading beech tree overhead to keep us cool.

'Boyzo,' Dad starts straight in. 'I don't think I will be seeing you this summer, unfortunately. Your mother is planning an Aegean cruise for you and your sister Julia. It sounds great fun and will be ideal for your sister as she can sit on deck with her wheelchair braced and take the sea air while you run around.'

I digest this news quietly. Yes, OK. That makes sense. But where will Dad be, exactly? In Wormwood Scrubs? Has there been a secret trial like a Star Chamber? Will I need to appear to give evidence? What has been the main reaction of the extended family? Has he been disowned by everyone he knows? There's also the question of some apology. There's years of puffing and blowing behind my back that needs some careful explanation. I sit and wait.

'I myself will be going on a long tour down the Nile and back. I should have liked you to come with me, boyzo. I'm sorry it can't happen but your mother thinks it's not appropriate just now.'

My father's eyes look ready to squeeze out a hidden tear. Is he kidding? Does he really think I could have gone with him down the Nile like some kind of emperor with his catamite?

'That means I won't be seeing you after today for… some time, boyzo. That's why I wanted to come today. To say goodbye for now.'

Dad grabs my hand and holds it tightly in his fingers. I can see how choked up he is. The tears are brimming round his eyes. I am deeply confused by that. This is rather like the scene you have in a movie between two lovers who must part: Brief Encounter or something like that. But I am sitting with my Dad. He runs his fingers gently up and down my forearm which makes the golden hairs bristle.

'You know how I love you,' he says as a matter of fact, looking at the players in the distance.

Yes, I think I can believe I do know. I am also trying to keep my eyes fixed on the cricket players who are spreading round the field. Two confident boys from the other team are coming out to bat. Perhaps I can will them to be bowled out on the first ball. I don't want the tears to flood my face.

'Yes, I know that,' I whisper.

Surely now the confession will come in all its harrowing detail. I hope it will be reasonably brief or we will both crack up under the strain.

'Boyzo...' Dad sighs. 'What can I do now? What can I say to you?'

I wait for his next words.

'I will always be here.'

'I know you will, Dad,' I murmur, still with my eyes fixed on the players. A bowler is coming up to deliver the first ball. It spins across the grass and there is a loud CLOK as the bat collides and knocks the ball a yard or two safely aside.

There is a long silence while we watch the game. COME ON, I'm thinking. I need to understand the madness of your love and how it happened. Dad clears his throat noisily and the seconds tick by.

'I hear your school has been winning more matches this year,' he eventually says in a normal voice. 'That's very good.'

'Yes, Dad,' I say faintly.

'Well done for that.'

He pats my hand as if the school's winning streak is all my doing and then he stands with creaking joints.

'Well, it was lovely to see you if only briefly, Robbie. It was worth the drive.'

No explanations then and certainly no apology. I walk with Dad in strange bewilderment back towards the school. You've got to ask him to apologize, I tell myself along the way. The questions should be put to him fair and square. Put them now before we reach the car. Why did you take off my pyjamas when I was only seven? Why did you get behind me when I was nine? Why bugger me on the side of the bed at eleven? But then the cricket master walks towards us to intercept. Dad's face looks composed as he thanks the man for the opportunity to meet and shakes his hand.

'Thank you. I must be on my way.'

Dad waves a last time towards me as he climbs into the Bentley before driving away. There is a fake smile fixed on his face that covers what he is thinking. I can't even guess if he is regretting not saying more to me.

There are so many questions here that I feel breathless; just as breathless as I was watching his car disappear. What did Dad mean by telling me how

123

much he loved me? What did he mean by asking what could be done? To go further back, what did Dad mean when he asked my mother to be aware of the beam in her own eye? Why didn't he tell me at least what happened between him and my brother when they held a discussion over me? Why didn't he say sorry then?

ONE: You've asked me a number of questions, boyzo. I'm going to give the answers after my own fashion. I told you how I loved you because that was the essence of what happened between us, which was that I lost my head. I was in love with you, yes. With others too, but you mostly at that time. *What can I do?* means, do I change my life or go on as I am now? People in love lose their heads and their life ambitions go to pot. That was the choice I had to make.

TWO: Adult business is not for discussion with small boys, however much they are owed an explanation. You knew already too many sordid details about me. That was my error. I wasn't going to add to that by giving you more. You are a worrier by nature like your mother. Did you think I was going to add fuel to your fire? Anyone could tell looking at your face that you were struggling with strong feelings of guilt and shame. It was up to me and others to sort out that mess. If you had been eighteen like your brother, maybe I would have explained more.

THREE: I was continuing to believe that what passed between us was not evil, only excessively loving. How can you define intensity of passion as wholly evil when it isn't? Our love was beautiful and sacred in its own right. It's convention that vilifies such relationships. What happened between us was overly extreme but not something to be punished with iron bars.

FOUR: Do you think your Mum rang the police as soon as your interview with her was over? Robert, you were only eleven years old. She needed time and careful consideration. What she did instead was to reach for her lawyer and her friends; her nearest allies. Their first question would have been to ask what could be proved. Nothing at all! Was she going to have your rear end examined by doctors for evidence of tissue damage? Of course not. Was she going to put you in the witness box when your eyes could hardly see over the railing? Certainly not. Was she going to give the newspapers a story they would carry on their pages for months? Even less likely. Think of the effect on your life with boys crowding round, asking you to show them your exact position on the bed. *Here's a pillow you can use in demonstration!*

Robbo, I am sorry to bring you this vision of reality but you may as well realize how the world works.

The padre actually cheered when he saw today that I had started on the painting. I had put in two hours solid before lunch after completing the writing about Dad's visit. There were also some complaints from Father P because I had allowed spots to fall across the terracotta tiles.

'It's difficult to avoid that,' I protested, 'when the ceiling's above your head and the damn roller drips. I'm lucky I'm not half blind by now.'

Unlike most monks, Father Perceval is not a great one for accepting explanations.

'You should have put down more newspaper,' he growled. 'Now you'll have to buy some turpentine and scrub the floor.'

I could have walked off the job then and there. It's funny how your temper swells – at least mine does – when you've been working hard and something still isn't good enough for someone else.

'When are YOU going to do some painting?' I asked him bitterly. 'Instead of listening to the caterwauling of a bunch of Roman orphans.'

Father Perceval cast those round bright eyes at me as if I was giving him ideas.

'They're getting really good!' he said. 'Today there was a lot of clapping at the café. What about that concert? Now you're doing up the big room it will be ready for the boys before long.'

I shook my head.

'No, thanks,' I said. 'The concert doesn't fit with my writing schedule.'

Father P thought for a minute about this before leaving the upstairs room. Then on the stairs he turned and looked at me.

'You know what?' he said. 'I think you're afraid.'
'Of what?' I scoffed.

'Of mixing with the world. Having the boys here is a case in point. I think you've got stage fright, Robert. We must study what to do about that.'

I reacted angrily but inside myself I knew what he was saying was true. I had been thrown off the roller coaster twice in a big way; the last time only a few weeks before. I was running scared. OK, the writing was a tough act to combine with anything but it was part of a defence mechanism. When was I going to engage again with life?

'OK,' I said recklessly. 'Invite the boys to come and play their songs. What do I care? Let them come and paint the walls too. We'll have a party and get drunk and share our beds as well. You'll enjoy that part.'

John comes upstairs to my room in London to see me a few days before the holiday in Greece begins. He has finished with Eton and is soon setting off on a tour abroad. He steps into the room while I am reading on my bed and walks up and down to the window and back to the closed door. At last I think I am going to hear some details I have been missing these vital weeks: what happened between him and Dad when he went for a confrontation.

'I have spoken with our father,' he says, making it sound a little like a prayer. 'I asked him if it was true, what you said to Mum and Doctor Scott about what happened. He said he had never done anything to you that caused you harm.'

My face is flushing red. Somehow I didn't foresee this answer from Dad. I expected he would admit to every detail. How could he deny the nature of his acts? My brother is staring at me as if I have got him in a heap of trouble by asking him to confront our father. It's the same doubt he showed me when I said I had jumped from that nunnery window.

'Dad did everything,' I say, beginning to feel tears starting to dribble from my eyes. 'He stroked me and kissed and sucked me and put a hankie over my bum and rode me...loads of times. Before the skiing trip in

January, he pushed his willy inside my bum about three inches.'

'It's impossible. He never did that,' my brother says firmly. 'He told me he never did you any harm.'

'I promise you, he did that exactly!'

I start to cry seriously.

'I think it's all exaggeration,' John says earnestly. 'Which you've always shown, making more of something than the strict truth. I've now had a quarrel with my Dad over you.'

'Well, I'm sorry.' My storm of tears appears to be having little effect on my brother. 'I haven't exaggerated anything.'

'I think so. That's why we're not doing anything about Dad. You can't be trusted to tell exactly what happened.'

I howl at these words. How can I have a brother who doesn't believe me? I look up to add more but it's too late. John has gone out of the room and slammed the door.

Well, no prizes for guessing who gets the questions today. The Dying Gaul had nothing on me at the moment John left the room. I felt as if I'd lost my brother's sympathy and love as well as that of the rest of the family. Why wasn't I believed? I couldn't understand. All I can do now is guess as no explanations have been forthcoming.

ONE: (John) I was feeling guilty for not stopping our father earlier. I couldn't admit this feeling to you and still can't but I guessed he might try SOMETHING with you at some stage because he had tried it on me at thirteen. I walked away, of course. But I wasn't expecting anything to happen to you so soon. How could I know? You said nothing. All the same I felt some guilt for not looking out. That was bugging me and explains why I got angry. Your exaggerations made me cross.

TWO: Why would you want to inflate actions that were already disgraceful – even stroking? To me that meant my younger brother was tainted and had become unclean. You were lucky I didn't slap you. If you had been a junior boy at Eton, I might have called you to the library for a thrashing.

THREE: I was a trifle jealous. Dad never gave me quite the same degree of cuddles he gave you. Yet I was the older son, the one who would inherit his estate. I should have held our father's full confidence and love, not my sneaky brother. I saw how you squirmed into his arms, particularly around Christmas. I detested that and so did my sisters. You were always looking for attention. That story about penetration was part of a pattern of wanting to draw people's sympathy; trying to make out you were always central. You have a complex there in my opinion that often affects a second son.

FOUR: Perhaps you don't realise the damage you have done to our mother by your exaggeration? I am closer to her than to my father and always have been. She tells me everything that's going on in her mind. You've practically destroyed her will to live with your wild claims. Mum is currently seeing a psychoanalyst every week to try to hold herself together. She's thinking this business happened because she was not living with us and taking care of you. You're the one who has given her the sense of blame.

Maybe John was not thinking any such thoughts. Maybe there was more going on in his life than I realized. If that's so, then why didn't he come and talk to me, rather than hide behind his ivory tower? I was left after that meeting feeling not only guilty but ashamed because my brother was convinced I was telling lies.

I decided to start at the bottom of the bedroom wall this morning and work upward, reasoning it will be easier later on if I am not bending down to reach the floor and leaving scuff marks on the owner's tiles. Also I was running out of paint and reckoned that to leave a skirting round the room was tidier than an uneven line higher up the wall.

As it proved, the skirting was a nightmare as I had to work on my hands and knees and use careful brushwork beside the tiles instead of the roller. It's amazing when you get your eye six inches from the corner of an old damp wall what evidence of insect life you find there: sudden beetles that scuttle out at you from hiding places and shake their pincers in your face; mouse droppings; spiders that appear from nowhere; ants and little fluttery moths that are probably after your clothes. Once or twice I plastered the struggling creatures to the wall with paint but that made me feel like an assassin. I became convinced I was building up more trouble for myself in heaven than by not painting the room at all. So I desisted and shooed the insects out of sight instead.

I wished I had a radio because silence in the castle is often VERY LOUD, if you know my meaning. I pictured all these ancient residents watching my work and bitching to each other. 'That young man does not know his arse from his elbow when it comes to paint.'

Tomorrow I will go down to the town, flourish the empty paint cans at the *mesticheria* and demand more. I may also pop into the café and see if I can find a telephone to call home. I'd like to hear my mother's voice if only to reassure myself she's not drunk. Of course I risk not having my voice recognised and having to tell her I'm her lost and wayward son in Italy.

'Oh darling, is that you? Call back later, will you, Rob? I'm in the middle of a picture and do you know what? I am liking what I'm doing.'

On the SS Romantica in Venice, Mum has found an old friend in Lady Astor, who smokes incessantly and covers herself in furs despite the heat. They spend most of the cruise gossiping about the old days on the political rostrum giving speeches in support of male opinions. This suits me fine as I have found an English friend my age to chat with. We fill the days sailing down the Adriatic playing deck quoits, gambling over horse races in the saloon and begging turns at shooting clay pigeons from a corner of the captain's bridge.

My sister spends the day sitting in a deckchair covered in rugs, reading Jane Austen novels to catch up with her English studies. It is hard to tell her mood because she doesn't giggle so much as before. She can hardly move without assistance and needs help eating as one side of her body is still partly paralysed. Sometimes Julia waves me over as I am passing for a private word. I guess by her secrecy she wants to talk more about what happened with Dad. I have a choice whether to submit or carry on chasing my friend.

'Why is it you never gave Kate and me a clue as to what was going on?' she asks when she gets me alone, with hardly a preamble.

The hoarse whisper from her throat can be hard to follow but I know at once what she's talking about. The subject is set in capitals inside my head.

'I thought you knew already,' I say. 'At least that Dad and I were taking baths together and I was going every morning to his room.'

'Of course not!' Julia responds robustly. 'If we'd known that, Kate and I would have been asking questions all the time and coming in to spy on you. We knew nothing. You kept it all a big secret inside your brain.'

She points to my head. The word secret adds to my sense of guilt as if it was my deliberate ploy; to turn the key in the lock on the rest of the world and keep people out.

'There was no secret,' I protest. 'Dad never even closed the door of the bathroom when we bathed. You could have seen us there together any time.'

'If we'd known you were there. Didn't you find what he did to you disgusting?'

'Not really. I've been used to it for years. I never played any part except to turn away when he tried to kiss me and refuse to touch him. I simply lay on the bed still as a mouse.'

My sister looks at me hard in that way she does when she is trying to detect a lie.

'Are you sure of that? Come on, give over. You must have encouraged him a little. You must have found it quite exciting, being touched.'

I consider how to answer her. By bursting into a fit of tears, perhaps that could avoid the necessity to find words. Questioning is not easy in front of a sobbing child with passengers having their ears flapping. Instead I whisper, 'I DID NOT!'

Julia is looking at me like the questioner looked at St Peter when the cock crowed.

I watch the islands off the coast sliding by, dusty brown and low to the water which is a purplish blue. The waves kick up white crests. I am thinking of Homer and the Iliad which I am studying at the moment in school. Meantime I am watching the poet's wine-dark sea. There are magical moments visiting what seems like the doll-sized wharves in Dubrovnik and Corfu; clapping my hands in a mountain glen so fifty thousand butterflies rise in clouds. Passing through the Corinth canal, I cross the deck from side to side to watch the railing of the ship slide past the walls, fearing we are about to crash into them.

In Athens when we visit the cathedral, there is a service in progress. Small boys throw twists of paper on the flagstones which explode like crackers while the priests are chanting. Incense is drifting in thick swirls through the air. A man approaches while I am walking on my own round the smooth-faced walls. He is a handsome bearded Greek in his middle thirties. My mother and sister are sitting in a pew, oblivious as usual to my fate.

'You are English boy?' the man asks with a broad smile.

'Yes, sir.'

'How old are you?'

'Eleven.'

'You are come here to see Athens?'

'Yes. I am seeing the city just today with my mother and sister.'

'Where are they?'

I point out the pew.

'I can show you all of Athens,' the man offers with a grand gesture. 'On your own, maybe is best.'

I consider this kind invitation.

'My mother would be worried. We have to get back to our ship by this evening,' I declare.

The Greek waves his arms in front of my face.

'That is not a problem,' he assures me. 'I can take you to your ship directly if you come with me first.'

I consider the offer. It sounds exciting but also mysterious and somewhat dangerous. What does an adult Greek man want with a small blond English boy? I should send him packing. Instead I smile.

'You want to show me what?'

'All of Athens,' he says, offering to take my hand and walk away together. 'I am very good guide.'

I can believe that – but on a tour of what? I shake my head regretfully and turn towards the safety of my mother. The man calls after me as I walk away. I feel I am disappointing him in much the same way as my father when I avoid his room. Back on the ship, I think what might have happened if I had gone along on the Athens tour. Surely I would have learned more about the ways of Greeks but would I have ever returned to the ship? I wouldn't have bet on my chances.

So my questions today are for that lusty Greek; let's call him Athos. I was half ready to go along with him because the man was solid and handsome and smiling with a twinkle in his eye. What kind of logic is that? Was that the way I was going to live my life in future? There was no excuse for such stupidity. It's clear I was still a prime target: blond and blue-eyed, slim and obliging. Perhaps I am so still though less now as I grow gangly. Perhaps a part of me still wishes to continue to follow men's wishes. Perhaps I should have a placard printed on my chest which reads: ASK ME TO COME WITH YOU – I WILL CONSENT.

ONE: I, Athos, am a normal Greek. I like young boys for the bedroom as well as women. It is many years since I indulged this practice as my wife will not agree. I saw you that day and took a risk. You invited me with your blue eyes the colour of the sky. You may not have realized and intended it but you did.

TWO: Something in your manner, English boy, attracts a grown man's attention. It is no coincidence that your father used you himself. You look ready to please; also a little lost and helpless, if I may say so. You trail your fingers along the cathedral wall as if you are dreaming of discovering more than just that surface in your life. It's a tempting prospect for a full-blooded man, especially a lusty Greek. What can you do to lessen the effect of this? Hide those blue eyes and do not let them shine. Learn not to look so lost, tossing your hair back in that artless way. Walk in a style that is more manly even if you are eleven.

THREE: Next time you see me, let me take you on my Athens tour. I will be kind and teach you everything. I will not slit your pretty throat. If you wish to return to your ship, I will bring you. No one need ever know the details of our tour. That is for us and the Gods to know.

Father Perceval was pleased to hear before he left this morning that I planned to call my mother today. 'Send her my regards,' he said, 'and tell her everything is going well, except your refusal to visit Rome more often than you do and your preference to mooch around the castle.'

'If I tell her that, she will be even more determined for me to take A-levels when I return,' I predicted. 'She's terrified of me drifting and doing nothing with my life. She's afraid most of all of DRUGS. That would mean to her that she has finally failed me as a mother.'

The padre gave me a slow nod to show I had guessed correctly. They must have had at least one face to face conference to discuss my situation before we came away to Italy.

'I don't understand you,' Father P said. 'Why won't you take A-levels at a crammer's in London if the exams would put your mother's mind at rest?'

I sighed.

'Because I don't see the temptation to climb back on the roller-coaster,' I said. 'I've been thrown off enough. What's in it for me?'

The Franciscan pawed his head, searching for convincing reasons.

'Don't you ever want a job?' he asked. 'Money, independence, position in society? You can't expect your mother to support you forever without quali-fications. Don't you want a girlfriend and a future marriage? You can't find any of these things sitting on your backside in a ruined castle.'

'Bleh, bleh!' I made a noise like a complaining sheep. 'Who says I WANT a girlfriend and marriage and a successful job? All that happens is you go off the rails eventually by doing something daft.'

'Such as what?'

'Going on an Athens tour with a lusty Greek.'

'What do you mean?'

'Never mind that.'

The café in the village had a billiard table at the back and I watched a group of teenagers playing an Ital-ian version of the game, using their hands instead of cues. I was waiting to use the café phone to call home. It had an international meter. But I needed a drink or two first to screw up my courage. Crazy! It took courage even to call my Mum.

The teenagers had this strange way of throw-ing one of the two white balls by hand so it would cannon into the red and then the other white. If they played it right, the ball would also knock into a ring of tiny mushroom ninepins in the centre of the table and mow them down. But if the central red ninepin was knocked over, there would be a groan from the boys on the player's side. He would receive penalty points instead of a plus score. I wondered why the adolescents were not in work or at college but standing round a billiard table. Perhaps they were wondering the same thing about me as I waited for the phone.

'Hi,' I said when I placed the call. 'It's me, Robert.'

Mum's housekeeper made a fuss about how wonderful it was to hear my voice.

'Wait a moment,' she said, 'while I call your mother.'

I waited while the seconds ticked away inside the machine.

'Hello, darling.' My mother came on the line with her careful voice as if I might bark at her. 'I was wondering when you'd call.'

'Did you get my postcard?' I asked, knowing I had only just sent it.

'Not yet. How are things going with you and Father Perceval?'

'We're just about on speaking terms.'

'Have you had a quarrel?'

'Not exactly. Let's say we have a different temperament.'

I had decided I wouldn't tell Mum he had tried to jump on me. What would be the point of that? It would only add to the deep well of her guilt. God, though, she knew how to pick my role models! At the same time I wasn't ready to say that Father P and myself were handing each other roses.

140

'What about the weather there?'

'Sometimes it's sunny and warm, sometimes cloudy and rainy. It's cold in the castle at night and pretty damp. But we survive.'

'What do you do during the day?'

This was a tricky question to answer. I didn't want to tell Mum about the writing because it begged the question of on what subject.

'At the moment I'm painting walls inside a bedroom on the first floor. It's eerie and I keep thinking I'm hearing voices from the Middle Ages: Lucrezia Borgia and stuff.'

My mum went silent for a moment. She was changing the subject in her mind because it was moving towards a complaint. I could hear the clicking of more than the telephone meter.

'Are you having good discussions?' she asked.

What she meant was, is the padre managing to reshape my world philosophy? Is he managing to get me to focus on my future life?

'Occasionally,' I told her. 'We chat about all kinds of things.' Now I was feeling mischievous; perhaps it was the drink. 'One conversation after dinner was about whether it's more fun to breed pigs or stick them up the arse like the British in India.'

My mother fell silent at that remark and I cursed myself for the heavy tease. Talk about sticking pigs up the arse to your mother? I don't think so. What I was saying, every time we spoke, was *are you feeling guilty? Can I twist the knife in your gut any more?*

'How's the family?' I asked.

'All well. Kate has announced her engagement in the press. Your brother is joining an aid charity to write articles. Julia has managed to enrol herself in a Montessori college to study as a teacher.'

I listened to the family news in silence, not feeling a part of the machinery. Not even a small cog.

'How are you?' I asked.

'Oh, I suppose I'm all right,' said my mother with that habit of hers of underplaying any high spirits. Was that a Scottish trait?

I could tell she was itching to put down the phone. So was I and there again I wasn't. I wanted to throw a hug down the telephone like a lifeline. I wanted to say I hoped she wasn't losing any sleep over my situation because I could take care of my-self. But I avoided saying anything she might have thought was a rescue attempt. She hated deliberate kindness.

'What day will you be home?' she asked suddenly.

'I think around the twentieth. You can expect me to be there for my birthday.'

'Well, have a good time meanwhile and toss a coin in the Trevi fountain for me for good luck.'

'Whose?' I asked as she hung up. But of course I didn't ring back to find out. She would have said yours, of course.

The autumn term has passed and I have been promoted to leader of the choir. I am still singing most of the solos. My twelfth birthday has come and gone and I am looking forward to spending the Christmas holidays in the Isle of Wight. Before New Year to my surprise Mum announces that I will be going to my father's house for a few days with my brother and sisters before next term. There's a big house party planned for New Year and important people coming from Parliament; my father wants me to be there as well. My sister Anne and her husband will be coming.

I am curious about how calm my mother is with this arrangement. Then I understand she's been exchanging more letters and telephone calls with my father behind my back. I hear one such conversation in progress while I am passing the sitting-room door.

'Hello, Hinch. Yes, Robert is here. He's looking fit and healthy. All ready to come down to you. How is everything at your end? Oh, I'm sorry to hear about the cook. I hope you'll find a replacement soon.'

No black bile, then, down the telephone or spitting into the receiver.

As a twelve-year-old, I am allowed to eat in the kitchen when I reach my father's house and not have supper delivered on a tray upstairs. I am allowed to walk through into the sitting room to join the ladies after dinner while the men are enjoying their port. On the Saturday night there is a fearful row between my brother-in-law and a Cabinet minister over politics. The men break up early and my brother-in-law walks into the sitting room to tell my sister to pack her bags. I watch as the government man follows red-faced and falls to his knees on the floor in apology. My father brokers peace. There are reconciliations. I am shooed upstairs by my sisters as though such scenes are not for my ears and eyes. It's curious to be reminded that I am still a child at a time when adult things are happening in bed.

In the night I toss and turn, thinking what fools politicians can make of themselves. I am seeing those red faces in the sitting room and comparing them to my father's exercising himself behind me. Is this all part and parcel of the desire in politicians to create challenge? Like mountaineers who feel they have to climb a different Everest every day.

In the morning the Cabinet minister leaves with his wife and chauffeur after an early lunch. After they've gone, Dad passes into the sitting room and we follow. He takes his cup of coffee and stirs it, then he walks over to my place and whispers hotly in my ear.

'Boyzo, will you come with me to take a rest?'

I look up in surprise. I glance round the room to see who has overheard. Nobody seems to be listening to us.

'What? Where?'

'In my study. That's where I go after lunch.'

'I can't, Dad,' I whisper in distress.

'Why not?'

I can't say I'm not supposed to be alone with him as no one has said so. It would be a lie. I sit where I am, looking frozen. Perhaps I should announce to the room that Dad has made a pass.

'Why not come?' he repeats in another whisper.

'Because I'm not supposed to,' I whisper back.

'Who says?'

'Everyone.'

I look round again, astonished that no one is aware of our conversation. Do my brother and sisters not care a whit what I do? Or is this a test to see how I will handle my father? Perhaps they have assumed I will say no as simply as if Dad has asked me on a walk. I know this won't be a simple rest. It will involve taking off my clothes.

'I'm sorry, Dad,' I mutter, feeling I am letting the man down. 'I can't come.'

He turns away with a look of dismay on his face. I am denying his love. I can see the sickness of it, the grieving in his eyes. But what can I do? If we resume, then I become something new and deliberate. I can no longer say I am only a loving son. I am more of a Ganymede, serving Turkish delight on a tray.

Questions, questions. I could put them today to that senior member of the government who drove away early. If I put them to my Dad, he will simply plead the usual excuses. I'd also like to know what the Cabinet man thinks about this odd licence to stretch the boundaries that belongs to members of the Parliamentary race. Does he think it's true that the country turns a blind eye to the extremes of its senior citizens? Or are we all truly equal under the law?

ONE: Robert, there does exist such an unspoken licence as you refer to. No one would dream, of course, of admitting the fact. But an informal licence exists in the armed forces, provided that officers don't go too far. It does even more so in public affairs. We are a trusting nation led by a Queen and that is why we have survived as a series of institutions. We never had a French revolution, nor come close to an industrial one. Our system is based on a unique model of privilege and compliance. It is true that some men use it to indulge themselves and the law is held somewhat in abeyance over them. This is unfortunate but true.

Your father is a good case in point. An unusual man: a clear thinker, a generous host and aristocrat. He's as brilliant in debate as William Pitt or Edmund Burke ever were and he has genuine enthusiasm for reform. There's no better man at whipping up his own side to fight some moral issue. But he has his weaknesses as many of us know well. He is obstinate and refuses to back down in argument. Many of his views are out of line with majority opinion. He is regarded by some as an old dinosaur who has outgrown his time. He can be petty and vexatious. It doesn't surprise me if he has acted towards you in some ways uncharacteristic of a father.

TWO: However, all that being said, I am distressed to hear that he chases his own son round the bedroom. I do know that he occasionally favours males – but not I hoped under-age boys. That is actionable in law and if he came before me on the bench, I would have no hesitation in sending him to prison - friend though he may be.

I have a second target for questions today and these are aimed at my brother and sisters. We were together in the house when I was twelve and onwards. The occasion I just described was the first time I had been staying with my father since the discovery of the bath. Was no one watching closely to see if anything would happen? Was no attention being paid to Dad's whispering? Was I being tested to see if I would accept him back? What would happen then: would someone would take camera shots of the action to gather evidence?

ONE: (John) Of course we were keeping watch. No one dreamed that Dad would ask you to go with him during a siesta. The audacity of the man is incredible. However it's also true that it was now your look-out. You were no longer an innocent. You knew right from wrong and we had shown our feelings of shock and horror. Being twelve, you don't expect others to tie your shoe-laces or watch where you are going down the corridor.

TWO: (Julia and Kate) We were still so shocked that anything could happen to our baby brother that we probably did continue to look away. Our darling Dad could not have acted as grossly as you described. He was so dashing and affectionate with young women who came to stay. If there was any misbehaviour, we would have suspected it was to do with a young wife or girl; certainly not with you. If darling Dad had truly done the things you said and we allowed ourselves to believe it fully, our world would have come tumbling down.

This evening Father Perceval and I had an unusual chat round the fire. I told him of my call home to my mother. He asked what she wanted to know about us. I said she had asked if we were enjoying some good chats. *Ah yes*, he muttered under his breath. *We should be having more of those.* We then went on to talk about my future.

'You must have SOME ambitions,' he put to me.

'Well, I do.'

'What are they?'

'I'd like to be married by the age of twenty,' I said firmly, having thought up this idea in the night.

'Why so soon?' Father P asked. 'That would seem a little young.'

'I want to become the opposite of Dad. If I don't start soon, I won't make it.'

The padre did his usual trick with his luminous brown eyes, making them round and appealing in their sockets by widening the lids.

'Oh,' he said. 'You think you're in danger of going his way?'

I stared into the fire.

'Well, what do YOU think?' I asked.

He gave a short laugh.

'Well, that's always possible. However you put up a strong defence against me when I approached you. I shouldn't worry about your manliness. I find it pretty convincing.'

I stared hard at a log in the fire.

'Do you think so?' I said. 'There are times when I don't agree. There are times when I don't think I have any resistance to my father's ways. I need to find a girl and marry early; cling to her and never let her from my sight. Otherwise I will grow up facing both ways.'

Father P made a noise like a horse blowing a trumpet.

'Robbie, you won't have trouble with that. Believe me, boy. You have roots growing in normal directions. And I should know something about that.'

It's a strange feeling to wake up in my father's house that spring when I go again at Easter, knowing there is something I should be doing when I check the time. I can feel my father's ache for me pulling at my umbilical cord. I can hear his echoing whisper reassuring me that the girls are fast asleep and will never know if I visit him again. There is no sibling visible or audibly patrolling the corridors. I could sneak in with Dad for a quick one if I wanted and the family would be none the wiser. The visit would please Dad enormously. I don't wish to face his sour face over the table at breakfast for another day.

Eventually my toes are tingling so hard out of a sense of filial loyalty that I force myself to stand and dress. It is only half past seven; time for the radio news. I steal downstairs and out of the house, avoiding the housekeeper and the new cook who have just arrived. I wander over to the wood yard and stare at the fence where I fell and hurt myself. I decide I will build a house up in the chestnut tree next to the fence and live there whenever I come to visit my father, out of reach of his siren calls. I might allow people to visit me but they must be only girls and pretty; also brave enough to climb up twenty feet to share my tree house.

On an impulse I rush back into the kitchen. I ask the cook's daughter who is sitting there to play outside with me. She is around ten years old.

'Can you climb a tree?' I ask on the way to the courtyard.

She tells me that she can't; however she doesn't mind watching while I do it. She is wearing a flowery dress and has pretty cheeks and fluffy hair like a doll's. I climb the tree with the girl watching me, going higher and higher in the branches. 'Be careful,' she calls out. 'You may fall!' I laugh and climb higher. 'You think that's impressive?' I shout down. 'That's nothing. Wait and see what else I can do.' Something has occurred that would excite my Dad if he was with us. I loosen the belt of my shorts and undo the buttons. The trousers start to ease down my hips. I invert myself and start slipping down the trunk, using my hands and feet and clamping the tree between my thighs. The shorts slip further and my pants start to follow them. The girl screams as if she is watching an ape misbehaving inside the cage of a zoo. I wobble convincingly as if I could fall. The girl screams louder and my pants come down the final inches. My willy pops out, straining and pointing like a cannon towards the ground.

'Robert, you're exposing yourself!' the girl calls excitedly.

'What do you mean?' I pretend innocence.

'I can see your willy.'

I glance under and see my penis staring down. The rubbing against the tree trunk has excited the muscle and it has never got so hard. How will I finish the scene? Perhaps I should let go and fall. That would be a perfect ending. The girl can reach out and touch my organ to console me but I'll be dead with a broken neck. Ideal!

However if I'm not dead she will tell the cook who will complain to my Dad. Quickly I lower my legs and stuff the offending organ in my trousers.

On another day before school begins, I walk up the tree-lined avenue towards the road to collect the newspapers from the wooden coffer beside the post-box. I can almost taste the crispy bacon and fried eggs that will soon be waiting on the dining room warming plate. As I walk, a boy appears on a bicycle and rides past the white-painted gate which is always open. I see he is holding the morning newspapers under his arm.

'Hello!' I greet him as the boy whistles past. He stops a moment with one foot on the ground. 'Are those our papers you're holding?'

'Yeah! I'm delivering them to his Lordship.' The boy is maybe a tad older than me and wearing a cloth cap.

'I'll take them,' I offer. 'I'm his son.'

The boy gives me a cheeky grin. He has longish, corn-coloured hair and is good-looking.

'Nope. It's OK. I have my orders, thanks.'

The delivery boy puts his foot back on the bicycle pedal. I watch him flying down the drive with the papers under his arm. Some instinct makes me walk after him quickly and then begin to run. I arrive at the front door just after it closes, seeing the bicycle propped up inside the porch. I turn into the sitting-room and cross into the garden hall. Glancing up the stairs, I watch the delivery boy crossing the red-carpeted landing towards Dad's bedroom door. He stands there and knocks lightly on the wooden frame.

'Papers, your Lordship.'

I sneak halfway up the first flight of stairs to see what happens next.

'Ah,' I hear Dad's voice as the door opens. 'Barney, I'm so glad you're here. Come inside and lock the door, will you, dear boy? That way we won't be disturbed.'

So – Dad – more questions for you.

When exactly did you replace me with the newspaper boy? Was it back in January as soon as I refused the rest? Was Barney as good at lying motionless as I was or was he more active? Probably that would be more fun for you. Did you love him madly like me or were your feelings simply physical?

ONE: What can I say, Robbo? You caught me red-handed otherwise I wouldn't need to reply. I could simply deny there was anyone at the door. You were always my favourite, dear boy. But you were no longer available to me and I had my needs. I know that sounds insensitive and it isn't meant to be: it's purely a fact. I had been warned off you. On top of that you turned me down when I asked. Barney provides for my needs in a splendid and spirited way; he obviously has previous experience. I hope I didn't disappoint you by taking a new boy but I couldn't help myself.

TWO: It must have come as a shock for you to discover there could be someone else; that my feelings for you were not exclusive. I'm sorry, boy. If it's any reassurance, I can tell you that you

153

were and are the most special person in my life, following your mother. However others can make effective substitutes. The heart can entertain a number of love objects. Human beings are made to be adaptable. I hope Barney didn't make you feel jealous and angry. He was more active, it's true. *But being more active wouldn't have made any difference to moving on.* That's my point. *Punto e basta*, as the Italians like to say.

I finished the coat of paint in the dormitory this morning by completing the middle section. There were a few more splashes on the floor. But what the heck, I had the first round of spots to deal with anyway. I reckoned I'd clear up the lot with turpentine once Father Perceval returned with the bottle from Rome. The *mesticheria* only had paraffin like that stuff I used on the ants. That wouldn't dissolve dried paint so I hadn't bought any of the stuff. I was so dog tired when I finished the painting that I just walked out of the room and took a bath, leaving the spots drying on the floor.

Now I'm feeling fresh and ready for another batch of writing. My exercise book is about used up. I will need another soon and wonder what the ones at the newsagents in town are like. Instead of ruled lines, they may have only blank pages that make it difficult to keep your lines in order. I always had a problem with writing without lines. 'Use a ruler,' I remember my teacher yelling. 'So your writing doesn't slope.' Did she ever use a ruler herself? It's tough to write when you're holding a ruler in one hand; like playing the piano with both sets of fingers going at the same time.

Now to prepare the sitting-room to receive the padre. I must redo the fire.

There's a new boy here who has joined the choir this summer. He has attached himself to me; maybe it's me who has taken him under my wing. Christopher is undeniably cute-looking and it's difficult to stop watching the boy when we are singing an anthem in chapel. He looks so fresh that God must be watching over him personally – but is He? There are dangerous people around, especially in a school like this one. I wouldn't trust the gym master, for example, when he's watching our underside against the floor.

The boy often volunteers to help clear up at the end of services. There are robes to fold neatly and put away after the choristers have used them. There are music scores to collect and file in the right places; hymnals and prayer books to return to the piles by the entrance doors. Chris does it willingly to please me and we chat about his home life and his sister at another school. He is shorter than me by a full head and wears his neat hair waved back so his ears stick out mousey pink.

I've been sent a present by my Dad that he brought back from a parliamentary conference in Tokyo. It is a six inch curved bamboo wand that pulls apart at the centre to reveal a dagger; a paper knife sharpened to a point. There is hieroglyphic writing on the handle that probably reads 'Welcome to Tokyo' or something similar.

I know the paper knife will interest Chris and put it in my jacket pocket to show him after chapel.

I watch the boy as he walks round the vestry tidying up after the others have gone. I am redressing and he is wearing his shirt and day trousers after pulling off his cassock. He is putting away the red and blue tunics the boys have cast down on the changing bench, spreading them out on the floor and carefully folding over the arms before making a neat bundle. I guess he is doing the job in the same methodical way his mother would have done. He probably also looks a lot like her with that brushed hair and slim form.

'What shall I do with these cassocks?' Chris asks, glancing up to catch my eye.

He has a honeyed tone in his voice and a whispery silkiness to it that is sexy. I am hearing it in much the same way as my own when I was nine.

'Leave them in a pile on the bench for housekeeping,' I direct.

I am noticing the boy's pert bum where it is bent over. Like mine at the same age, it is well rounded and quite small. The crack between the cheeks is well defined and I feel shocked by that exposure as if it is a personal affront. Surely Chris must realise it isn't safe to show your bum crack too clearly. I should administer a tiny correction to teach him to be more cautious.

Slipping the bamboo wand out of my jacket pocket, I withdraw the blade and approach the boy from behind where he is bent over, busily folding and stacking the cassocks in a tidy pile. I bend over his back and stab Chris lightly between the shoulder blades. It is only a pinprick; less deep than that compass thrown in my back when I was his age. The boy immediately gasps and freezes before turning to glance back at me.

'What did you do that for?' he croaks, turning white. 'What have you stuck into me?'

'Nothing much,' I say airily, sheathing the blade which I see has entered the skin like a drawing pin, leaving a small red stain on his shirt. 'It's a present sent me from Japan by my Dad; a paper-knife. I did that to teach you not to stick out your bum in the vestry. It's not right.'

I show Chris the paper knife while he's still making shuddering gasps.

'I'm sorry,' I mutter as the lad starts to cry. 'I shouldn't have stuck that in you. It was wrong. But you did slightly ask for it.'

I guess the questions today should be addressed to me. In the whirlwind of emotions, I felt deeply shocked and ashamed at what I had done; also worried the boy would report the incident. What was the meaning of my act? I was unable to sleep a wink for several nights, trying to work it out. I'm still a little unsure of the full meaning.

ONE: I was being reminded of myself aged seven and upwards, exposing my bum to Dad. He worshipped it and proved that many times over the years. I didn't want Christopher to follow in the same direction by tempting me. Therefore I stabbed him to prevent that happening. QED or *quod erat demonstrandum,* as every poor sod who has studied

Latin knows. At least I think the logic went something like that.

TWO: I was beginning to look at Chris with my father's eyes, wasn't I? Seeing what he saw and plotting what sexy response he could devise. I couldn't have that poison spreading in my blood so I hurt the boy to cut it out. There's the full analysis. If I hadn't driven the boy away, soon I would be unbuttoning his trousers. I feared the contagion like a vampire's bite; it might soon have me searching the dormitories at night. So I was forced to act.

Father Perceval was so pleased that I had finished painting the big room that he insisted on opening a 1.5 litre flask of Chianti when he came home tonight. He toasted me while the chicken was roasting in the oven and we lit a huge fire in the sitting-room and tossed back a few glasses of Tuscan red. Pretty soon I was feeling tipsy and ready to own up even to what happened with Christopher. Father P would have been fascinated by that tale. He might have added to the saga by telling me about his own temptations in the seminary when he was in training.

'So now the main upstairs room has been finished, we can confirm the weekend for the boys,' the padre announced with a look of triumph. 'What about next weekend? You have to leave for home soon after. I'll bring the boys over on the Friday night and take them back to the orphanage on Monday early. We can print some posters and spread them round the village during the week. You know the sort of thing: ITALIAN ORPHANS IN ROCK CONCERT AT THE CASTELLO. That should fetch the curious in town.'

I made a face I hoped would put him off.

'They're more likely to stone us with rocks and ask for their money back.'

'We'll only charge a pittance,' said Father P. 'Five hundred lire; something like that to cover basic costs. We can hire a pair of amplifiers from somewhere local. Would the café have them?'

I stared at the padre in dismay. 'I can ask. But why do we have to go ahead with the plan at all? I prefer the peace of the castle as it is. I don't want it disturbed by a bunch of teenage hooligans.'

Father Perceval took my hands as if he wanted to dance round the fire together. His face was glowing from the Chianti.

'Come on,' he insisted. 'Lighten up, Robert. The place needs some music and you do too. We need to bring in some fresh air.'

I gave the padre another doleful look.

'You haven't even asked the owner if it's OK,' I said. 'I'm sure it isn't and he'd say there's no way he would give permission. A concert would invalidate the insurance cover.'

'I'll ask the housekeeper to contact the man tomorrow,' the Franciscan said. 'I doubt very much he'd say no as long as we take good care of the arrangements.'

Maybe Father P was right. Maybe getting in a hectic mood would help lighten my mood which was feeling black. As it was, my writing wasn't much helping to prepare me for the prodigal's return to London.

'There are one or two conditions,' I said, holding up a wobbly finger and my glass, which needed a recharge. 'I'm not going to spend my days beforehand cleaning up the castle. I'm not even going to sell tickets around town. I'll ask for amplifiers and spread around some leaflets for the show. But only as long as the owner gives permission.'

'DEAL!' the padre exclaimed, pouring me another glass. 'Agreed without any reservations. Now swallow that last drop of wine and smile.'

I have fallen into a deep malaise at school over the shameful episode with Christopher. It's not helped during the autumn term by discovering that I am now able to obtain an erection whenever I want one by climbing the ropes in the gym. They hang down from the twenty foot ceiling like props in a circus act. I have discovered that if I swarm up to the top, it has the same effect as that tree trunk between my thighs when I was showing off to the cook's daughter. My organ swells inside my shorts until I am amazed it is not visible from outer space. A glow heats my genitals and spreads through my lower parts until I am left hanging and grinning like a monkey, wondering whether I will fall or pass out in bliss. If I do, it is highly probable my throbbing organ will be left exposed for all to see, lit up like the Dong with the luminous nose.

I go to see the chaplain again after a confirmation class. The bishop will be coming in the run up to Easter to make the senior boys full members of the Christian church.

'I don't think I'm ready to be confirmed, sir,' I say bluntly.

The chaplain looks at me with shock horror. I am leader of the choir and in that sense his leading boy. I must be confirmed at all costs.

'Why not? You're a prime candidate, Robert. You can't back out. What kind of lead would that give the other boys? What's the matter with you, anyway? What's the problem?'

I sigh heavily. How can I go into this discussion with the candour it requires?

'I don't think I'm fit, sir.'

'Why not?'

'I have sinful thoughts.'

The man stares back at me. I hope he's not going to burst out laughing and make fun of the idea of me sinning.

'My dear boy,' he says, searching for my knee with that polishing hand. 'We all have such thoughts sometimes: every one of us. We're only human. God recognises that. No one can fully renounce the devil within.' He smiles at me encouragingly. 'What makes you say you have sinful thoughts? Tell me more.'

I struggle to find words and am aware of my face turning bright pink.

'I think in the night time about…bums and penises, sir.'

The clergyman pats my knee.

'We all do, boy, if there are no girls about. Later on hopefully you will find you are thinking about females.'

'I doubt it, sir. You see, I've had an unusual upbringing.'

The chaplain looks glassy-eyed as if he has better things to think about than my home life.

'I don't wish to talk about that,' he says. 'We all have odd upbringings if you want to look at them in *detail. But God pardons the past and still admits us to His Church. I'm glad you have misgivings, Robert. That shows you are a true Christian, facing your responsibility in standing up to the devil.' He coughs into his hand. 'I suppose you've started masturbating, boy. You're the right age for that.'*

'Not quite, sir,' I say, dismayed by the assumption. 'I'm still not capable of…what you're saying.'

'But that stage is fast approaching, if you're thinking about bums.' The chaplain taps my knee again. 'It's totally understandable. Just remember that God knows all things. He's not concerned with minor fantasies.'

'I've been seriously sinful in the past,' I stammer.

Now the vicar does begin to laugh.

'Twelve years old and you wish to confess to serious sin!' He stands up. 'I'm not hearing your full confession, Robert. I'm not a Catholic. Dismiss the worries from your mind. You're my leading chorister. Don't miss out on the confirmation classes. I am relying on you to be the strongest candidate.'

Who's going to answer the questions crashing and tumbling inside my head? Obviously I should not have been confirmed at twelve and was unfit to be a member of the Anglican Church. In the run up to Christmas and Easter, I was looking increasingly at boys and wondering about their performance in bed. What would they feel about sharing their bodies? I was not helped by a circle of night adventurers that formed a group to experiment on the floor of the dormitory. The group would meet at midnight and form a circle to practise fellatio on each other. At other times the top performers would give a master class on ejaculation.

So, vicar, answer me this. If you had lain with your own father through most of your childhood, would you have wished to be blessed by the bishop? Would you not instead have been thinking of hanging yourself from the roof beams with the cord of your dressing gown?

ONE: Robert, if I'd had the sense to ask about your childhood in detail when you invited discussion, I might have sympathised. But I was in a hurry to get ready and panicked by your threat of revelation. I was nervous of the bishop and the big occasion. The chairman of governors was coming. So I was in no mood to help you – I do apologize.

As for the question of what I would have done in your position, I would have gone to talk to someone professional. I am very surprised your mother had not brought you to a therapist. She must have known you were struggling with guilt. Perhaps she thought you were too young to have such discussions. But you had been left to cope with an enormous degree of shame. It's extraordinary that no professional help was provided.

TWO: If my thoughts had been drifting in the same way as yours, I hope I would have had the maturity to ignore them. It's a phase we all go through approaching puberty: proto-homosexuality. It means nothing in terms of later influence. An expert would say anyway that your thoughts at that age were not developing in the usual gay pattern. If they had been, you would have been more likely to dream about the gym master or the swimming coach than boys. What a pity you were not seeing a professional who could have reassured you about that.

This morning the padre was on at me to read him a sample of my work before he left for Rome. He also informed me when I came downstairs that he had been already next door with the housekeeper discussing the concert plan. The lady was all for the project and we should know soon if it was OK with the owner.

'I'm not going to read you anything now,' I told him. 'Go to Rome and spend your day doing whatever it is you do. Today I will read over my manuscript and see. Maybe tonight I will find something interesting to read to you. But please don't think that means you're going to hear everything. There's no way I'm sharing most of my stuff with you.'

Father P had to be content with that.

It is the summer term of my last year at prep school. My mood has worsened to the point when I am wondering seriously about going on. My thoughts have reached a crisis point of confusion. My body has reached a crisis point of longing but is still unable to find physical relief. The spectacular orgasms that others enjoy continue to escape me. I am considering how to die. A rope inside the gym is one possibility. It would be highly effective if I could tie a knot and hang the rope round my neck, then shin up to the roof and take a leap. Another method would be to walk into the high street and time a dash across the road to coincide with the passing of a bus. A third method, which would have the advantage of being pain-free, would be to walk into a chemist's shop and persuade them somehow to let me have three packets of Aspirin.

I am walking down the aisle of the chapel after cleaning up the vestry – without Christopher's support now – when without warning I hear a thunderous voice echoing from the rafters thirty feet above my head.

'THIS IS MY BELOVED SON IN WHOM I AM WELL PLEASED!'

Is this some friend playing a joke who has somehow got hold of a megaphone? There is no one sitting on the crossbeams, nor some odd box up there that could be described as an amplifier. At once I start to shiver violently. What is going on? I feel enveloped with a radiant light that fills and illuminates me like a Christmas tree. I realise the voice must have been speaking from inside my head, not outside it. How can this be? Is it God speaking? Is it HE who is well pleased with ME? I have done everything to deserve His displeasure. God must have gotten hold of the wrong boy. He has spotlighted the wrong Beloved Son.

I totter the remaining steps to the chapel door and twist the handle open. Outside in the hallway boys are walking about as usual. One or two stop to exchange a few words with me. I am surprised they don't notice I am lit up like a beacon. If it was night time, I would surely be visible across Oxford. The heat my skin is giving off is terrific. Yet the boys talk about today's cricket scores and homework and other mundane matters as if nothing has happened. They don't notice my face which is like St Sebastian's, suffering but ecstatic. I wonder if I should point out the change. 'Do you see anything odd about me, guys? Well, the fact is God's just given me the odd news that I'm His Beloved Son.' If I say such a thing, the others will run off to report that I've gone crazy.

No, I must move about my business without comment or outward sign of any kind. I must keep my glowing entirely to myself; not even write home to announce the news. Who will believe that? It will be another case of Robert's powers of exaggeration. However if that voice was not from God, then whence came the sound? Not from me; not from my father either. In my dormitory, I begin to put the change into quiet effect. I sing a lullaby to help people go to sleep instead of exercising their lusty organs. The boys are scathing of my attempts to sing them musical ditties; however they quickly adapt. From then on my singing becomes de rigueur. The boys call out numbers like tunes on a juke box and I have to sing the requested tracks. To my mind, it is the least I can do to show God He is merciful to me and I am grateful.

There is no one in this ruined castle that can answer my questions today except God Himself. Not even the Pope can answer on His behalf and certainly not Father Perceval. Was the message that resounded from the rafters created in heaven?

ONE: (God) Of course it came from me, dear boy. I was well pleased with you. You had done no wrong apart from the minor incident with Christopher. You had not gone padding round the beds at night but remained shivering inside your own. You had also refused your Dad when he whispered so silkily in your ear. I didn't want you to hang yourself from a rope. What would have been the point in that? Another wasted human life at a time when help is needed. Oh yes, we were developing plans for you, my son. The heavenly council is very good at making plans.

Messages that sound like claps of thunder echoing from the rafters of a church are something we can easily achieve in Heaven's workshops. We can make them sound like they are inside your head. We can also create burning bushes and do wondrous things with water and with lightning. They all look like the miracles they are designed to emulate. They ARE miracles, if you like. However if you look closely, the action is all done with lights and sounds like a *son et lumiere*. The burning bush is inside your imagination, stimulated by the heating of your brain.

TWO: My message to you is to stay on course, dear Beloved Son. You have gone through your Confirmation. Your family and godparents have gathered round in a church service to ward off evil. Make use of that for godly ends. Even your father was there, chanting his responses and deluding himself about his innocence while drying his tears with that big white handkerchief of his. Hold firm and keep yourself pure, my dear. You will come through to salvation.

This evening I read the first chapter of my book to Father Perceval while he was sitting with his feet tucked up in front of a roaring fire. His sandals were under his round bottom and he was wearing a change of robe after his bath with a slightly lighter shade of brown to the material. I missed out the part about how the padre had jumped on me outside the bathroom on the first night. That would have upset Father P, to say the least. However I read about the reasons I thought Mum and Dad had divorced; the highly personal *burn at the stake even for saying it* ones. Father P's eyes popped open as I read the chapter until his eyebrows were practically crawling off his face.

'Wow!' he said when I had finished. 'That's strong stuff to say about your parents. What are you going to do with this manuscript when you're done?'

'Probably I will burn the thing,' I said.

'How far have you got so far?'

'Around halfway. I've just finished with my life up to the age of thirteen. The second section will deal with the recent years at Eton.'

Father P looked almost frightened by the prospect.

'So you'll be putting things about me in there?'

'Oh yes.' I gave a short laugh. 'Don't worry. You'll play your part when it comes to it.'

'You'll make nice comments, I hope,' the padre said with one of his weasel looks at me.

'You'll have to wait and see.'

PART TWO

The boys in my tea group are the ones I get to know best in my first few weeks at Eton College. Jeremy is like a small, bright bird. He has beautiful cheekbones and extraordinary arched eyebrows. I fall in love with him on the spot. Martin is more plain-faced but fun and has mousey brown hair. Thomas is shy and white-haired, with glasses like a scientist. It is usually Jeremy who dominates the conversation because he has his mother's wit and her cocktail hostess laugh. We tell each other annotated versions of our family history and how we came to be there. 'Oh, were you at Summerfields?' asks Jeremy. 'A friend of mine went there for a while and said the gym master was continually trying to fiddle with him.' Thomas talks least. He watches us speak and chews on his cereals like a rabbit munching lettuce. Martin seems eager to please and is always handing round toast and butter with a dazzling smile.

There comes a sudden interruption. A senior puts his head round the door.

'What are you doing sitting at tea, all of you? Didn't you hear the Boy's Call?'

'No, sir,' we say, standing up as you must do when a member of Library arrives.

'Well, jump to it. Liddle just gave a call. He's at the other end of the corridor. You'd better run or you'll be on the beating roster, all of you.'

175

We hare down the corridor to the place where Liddle is standing, tapping his fingers impatiently against the wooden panelling. There are four boys already waiting in a line.

'Come on. You're late!' he shouts at us.

Generally it is the last who runs the errand but for some reason he picks out me. I am standing next to the bespectacled Thomas.

'You'll do for this job, Montagu,' he says, casting a regretful eye at Jeremy further up the line. He produces a piece of paper folded over several times and bent into the form of the letter 4. The flaps are folded in such a way that the message is held securely. 'Take this to Fellowes in RDC. Wait for a message to bring back.'

I want to say, what, right now in the middle of my tea? And why not Thomas who was last? But I must do what I'm told or accept an appointment with the cane. To do the job more quickly, I half run to the house which I have learned by constant repetition is RDC and run around looking for a boy called Fellowes. I find the senior having tea with others in the Library. I hold out the message. I am breathless but I hope not visibly trembling.

'This is for you. From Liddle in PSHL.'

The boy opens the note, glances at me up and down and smiles knowingly. He passes the message round the group at the table and waits for them to comment. They also look me over carefully. One of them beckons me for a closer inspection.

'What's your name?'

'Montagu, sir.'

'Bend over, will you, Monty, and touch the floor with your fingers. No…facing away from me.'

I do what I am told, feeling somewhat confused by the request.

'OK. Now stand up. Not bad but not perfect either.'

More titters are exchanged between the group of boys. Fellowes stands and goes over to the escritoire in a corner of the room. He writes a long reply on the bureau and folds the note while the boys are asking me more questions. He brings the message over, presented again as the figure 4.

'Take that back to Liddle with my compliments,' he says, then adds with a smile. 'We may be seeing more of you, Monty. Who knows.'

Three weeks into the first half, I take my knowledge test in the Library standing in front of the seniors. There are seven of them. What is the name of the house on your left as you walk through Judy's Passage? What are the house colours of CPD? On what date in the year is Founder's Day? How long would it take you to walk from School Office to Provost's Lodge? Some of these are trick questions designed to trip me up. If I say ten minutes to the last, then everyone will laugh because the places are close by. All the boys are holding canes that they are busy thumping against cushions on the floor or the side of their armchairs. You are only allowed two questions wrong out of ten – more than that and I will receive six strokes of the cane. I have already got two wrong.

'What do you call a boy in school clothes who wears a fancy waistcoat in the street?' asks one of the senior boys, a handsome type who seems to be flirting with a thin moustache. It is the last question of the set.

'A fancy waistcoat?' I repeat, searching my brain for clues.

'Don't repeat our questions, boy, just answer them!' thunders the Captain of the House.

'Would he be a member of a club, sir?'

'What sort of club?'

'A sports club?'

The seven canes whack out a steady rhythm on the cushions and armchairs. My bottom clenches at the thought of being struck if I get another answer wrong.

The boy who has asked the question makes a popping noise with his mouth. He does it again and the others turn on him in fury.

'Ssssh! Don't give the game away, Gus. The boy's about to be beaten.'

This gives me a clue and so I search for a memory connected with the popping.

'He's a member of Pop, sir!' I say excitedly.

A groan goes up from the group of boys and someone throws a cushion at the one with the beginnings of a moustache.

'You're lucky!' declares the Captain of House, dismissing me. 'You have narrowly escaped the cane, young Montagu. Send the next boy in.' He nods towards the door. 'AND NO CONFERRING, otherwise you will be caned anyway.'

One of the intentions of a public school is to shake up your wits just when you think they are becoming unscrambled. The idea is to force you to find your way in a new hierarchy when you have become familiar with the last. The teaching is designed to give you practice at fighting your way uphill in life like a sperm cell towards an egg. It's your duty to burst open the egg and stamp your imprint on it. You will need the experience, the theory goes, when it comes to Working in the City and Making Your Way in Life.

That's all fine and dandy if your home life is stable. If like mine it isn't – as in many chaotic families - then the experience of being thrown back into the deep end is a torture pure and simple. It is adding another set of traumas to those you have already. A body may begin to wonder if it's worth the trouble. A few do not in many boarding schools. You listen to the canes running down the corridors at night announcing a new flogging and you wonder if this one is meant for you. *What have I done? Have I failed to scrub my teeth with sufficient energy? Am I now going to be lashed like a midshipman on an eighteenth century warship?* You hear the yell of a Boy's Call and you wonder if it's time for the second visit to Fellowes and his mates. This time perhaps the guys will strip you naked.

I do have questions for various people here. Let's start with those seniors like Fellowes. Were you seriously thinking of using our bums for target practice?

ONE: The Boy's Call has always been a traditional method of serving up good-looking new boys to your friends. These days the going rate for a sexual service is two and sixpence; half a crown in other words. It's common currency in the school. Any further arrangement is up to the individuals concerned. Usually the younger boys go along with the request if the experience is pleasant. They make sure they're not last in line for a Boys' Call if it's not.

A question for my parents now – especially my father who should be an expert on such matters as this. Were you aware of this level of savagery going on at Eton? Did you foresee that I might be fagged to another house for sexual purposes or attacked in my own room for the same purpose? Was this part of the preparation for life you wanted me to experience?

ONE: Of course not, boyzo. Mum and 1 had no idea that such activities existed and I'm sure you exaggerate them. They were only gossip. How could you dream I could be so wicked as to plan that outcome for you after the relationship we enjoyed? Having said that, you'd reached an age when you need to go through some adolescent training to become a fine adult. Everyone has to do that and boys will sometimes be boys. Some are cruder than the average and you have to contend with that. No room for molly-coddling when you are thirteen.

Frankly – so what if you and your friends were sometimes asked to join in sex? A surprising number of us learned that game in one form or another, either at school or in the army. In some ways schools are the most appropriate place. You don't have to remain that way afterwards if you don't want. You can go on to enjoy women instead. What you do in your spare time at bachelor parties or on holiday is another matter.

The padre stood up to place more wood on the fire. The flickering flames were casting shadows on the dim lit wall even though the lights were on. In this place the few bulbs hardly glowed with the amount of electricity pushed through them.

'That stuff you read me about your father and your grandfather,' he said. 'I can't truly believe that.'

I shrugged.

'It makes sense. My sisters have told me about George at various times. It was lucky he didn't come near them when they were growing up. Certainly he molested both my aunts. One of them has already hinted that to me. It seems logical he did the same with Dad. The obsession over me had to come from somewhere real. I don't believe these things happen by chance.'

Father Perceval stomped back to his armchair and tucked his sandaled feet up in their usual place. He shook his head as if to clear the air. For a hopeful moment I thought he might go on to say something about his own experiences but instead he remained quiet.

'Can we talk more about next weekend's concert?' he asked at last. 'Permission has come through from the owner. There are some jobs to be done ahead of time.' The padre took one look at my face and wagged a finger. 'I will keep your tasks to a minimum. We need to prepare a poster for advertising purposes. I thought we'd write the words and sketch out the format before we go to bed. That way I can run the artwork through the orphanage printer tomorrow. You will need to visit the café and ask about an amplifier. Then there's the question of chairs and glasses and booze for the day itself.'

I groaned loudly.

'Enough. You promised to let me have some peace and quiet for my writing.'

The mad monk made his usual gestures in the air.

'I will. But arrangements still need to be made.'
'OK, OK.'

My knuckle hovers next to the woodwork on my housemaster's study door. I am fifteen. I look at the grain in the wood and have a flashback of the times I have stood before a similar white-painted door, at seven-thirty in the morning.

Tap, tap.

'Come in.'

I enter and reveal myself. What's visible to the housemaster is probably a thin, worried face above a body which is insufficiently nourished. A sort of Dickensian weasel figure.

'Robert.' The grey-haired man lifts his head from a contemplation of his littered desk. 'What can I do for you?'

I walk across the Persian carpet and deliver a piece of my homework that has been scribbled on with a red pen.

'I was asked to bring you this, Mr Lawrence,' I say uncertainly.

'I see. A red pen.' The housemaster puts on his spectacles so he can see who it is from. 'From Mr Massie, your history beak.'

'Yes, sir.'

The housemaster lifts his mild gaze to me. I am not sure if he can see my figure clearly with the specs or if I'm a convenient blur.

'How many red pens does that make this half?'

'Two, sir. One in Maths and one in History.'

'One more red pen and I'm supposed to send you to the headmaster to be beaten.'

'Yes, sir.'

I stand looking past the man at his private lawn outside the window. No ordinary boy is allowed out there. Only the seniors are permitted for tea in the summer, when they might catch a glimpse of one of the housemaster's pretty daughters.

'I don't know what it is with you, Robert,' says Mr Lawrence. I realise he is still looking at my face. 'You don't appear interested in the curriculum and yet you are perfectly capable of good work. You have turned in excellent pieces in the past when you have wanted: especially in English.'

'Yes, sir,' I say.

'Maybe a thrashing from the headmaster is what you need,' the man goes on. 'It would make you pull your socks up. At the moment you are too concerned with meddling in other boys' lives.'

'Yes, sir,' I say. I know this litany off by heart. I have tried appealing to this figure of authority many times to reign in the sexist thugs he has put in charge but he seems helpless or unwilling to cooperate with someone who is still a junior.

'The next red pen you receive,' Mr Lawrence says sternly, 'I will do my duty and send you to the HM. I should warn you he takes beating very seriously. I don't need to ask him to lay on the cane.'

I nod. Perhaps I have misjudged my housemaster. Perhaps he is not a push-over in the hands of brutal prefects but a fellow traveller.

'Now go.'

I don't say another word. I leave the study and close the door. I am picturing just how a lashing from the headmaster will make me pull my socks up. Will he tickle my calves with the cane during the process and, by hooking the handle through the socks, yank them higher? The thought makes me smile as I ascend the stairs. I tap at Jeremy's door and walk in while the boy is getting dressed for games. He spins round in sudden alarm.

'Oh God! I thought it was an enemy raid.'

He releases his arms. His breasts flop loose. It is not, of course, by any means the first time I have seen the womanly glands. We have spent whole hours discussing Jeremy's particularities: the assets and disadvantages of possessing boobs in a place like Eton.

'I had my meeting with Wettie just now,' I say.

'What did he tell you?'

'One more red pen and it's the HM for me. He said I needed the cane to pull up my socks. It made me laugh after I went out, imagining the idea in action.'

Jeremy hands me a swathe of bandaging. 'Wrap me up, will you, Rob? Good and tight.'

I wind the bandage across his breasts and round his back, applying the disguise in such a way that the strapping will not show under the open-necked rugby shirt.

'You must keep up the revision,' Jeremy advises me. 'You don't want to be flogged by the Oick.'

'I'm too busy to revise,' I say. 'I had a session with Martin earlier that had me seriously concerned about his mental health. There's also a new boy I'm worried *about who has been skulking in his room for no good reason. I also said I would pop in to see Philip after tea to help with his low mood.'*

Jeremy strips off his grey trousers and pulls on his shorts, turning sideways to preserve his modesty though I know his body is still as hairless as when he was born. Meanwhile my body has completed the change from boy to man; much good the maturity has done me, as the ability to ejaculate seems only to cause more anxiety.

'I must get going,' Jeremy says. 'Let me know if you want me to visit that new boy. Someone may be getting at him in some way. What's his name?'

'Samways,' I say. 'How are your rehearsals for As You Like It?'

Jeremy makes a face as he pulls on his rugby socks.

'The fitting of my clothes for the part of Rosalind has been interesting, to say the least: quite a joke for some fellows in the cast. I hope they're going to be discreet.'

'Do you want to try out some lines?'

'Not now.'

The boy waves cheerfully as he goes towards the door.

'Pray for me on the sports field and hope to God that no one decides to give me a flying tackle.'

I return to my room at the far end of the corridor. It occupies a corner of the boy's wing, looking down on the housemaster's gravelled drive. The room is festooned with paper fishes in the Japanese style that swim across the ceiling. On the wall there is a poster of a Spanish bullfighter and below it a genuine matador's sword that I have been allowed to hang as a decoration. I may

186

be the only schoolboy in England with a lethal curved matador's sword in its red leather scabbard hanging on my wall. Inside a secret drawer of my writing desk there are numerous A4 files pushed to the back. They have boys' names written across the corners. There is a yellow one with Martin's name on it that I pull out. Inside are many sheets of handwriting; my detailed accounts of his disturbing dreams. I enjoy trying my hand at interpretation. This is helped by having Freud's 'The Interpretation of Dreams' sitting fatly on the shelf above my writing desk. Next to that is another large book on Quotations. If I look up the words: "WHOSO – SHALL – OFFEND – ONE – OF –THESE – LITTLE – ONES – WHICH – BELIEVE – IN – ME…' I shall find the text well thumbed. I don't need to highlight the text with a pen as the book has learned to fall open at the spot.

What I have done for myself over the intervening years is not clever or original but it seems to work for me. I have diverted my guilt over my own abuse into a calling to help others. By spending my time thinking about them, I have managed to draw attention away from the mess within me. That's the theory. I also operate an alternative surgery to Matron's whereby I administer plasters for cuts and ointments for spots. There is a lurking bottle of aspirin for headaches and disinfectant in case of need. The main purpose however is to treat emotional disturbance. Most boys have some problem they are trying to hide. Some are living with the results of rape. Some are in terror of being molested.

Some are fearful of becoming perverts themselves and they admit to their fantasies while sitting in my chair. Others have troubles at home: separating parents, cruelty between siblings, sorrows over bereavement and so forth. I try to bring a little comfort to make everyone feel brighter. I also conduct group sessions and hypnosis.

My method of making someone unconscious is horribly dangerous. I select a willing victim such as Jeremy who enjoys doing this for a laugh in front of an invited audience. I cause him to faint by crouching and fast breathing exercises, compressing the spinal cord and then the chest. The boy is then conducted by quiet persuasive words into a trance state. I talk with him in that way for a few minutes and then he wakes with a stream of post hypnotic suggestions planted in his mind. To take one example, five minutes to the second after he wakes Jeremy may suddenly recognise my top hat as a birthday cake. He will offer to pass slices round the audience and go from one boy to the next presenting so-called pieces of the hat while the boys stifle their giggles. There is no threat to my smart hat. The boy makes the motion of cutting with one hand and dishes out the slices with the other with his fingers clutching the air. The watchers are amazed and clap. I sign up more visitors to discuss their problems face to face. They return to their rooms refreshed and ready to take on a difficult essay on the French revolution.

The personal benefits of giving therapy are that I have no more thoughts of suicide. I can sublimate my father's desires into a devotion to the cause of protecting others. I fall endlessly in love but hold myself rigorously in check. I remind myself that I am now serving a non-erotic master. God is directing my actions and His angels are watching everything I do. Heaven does exist even in the midst of despair and anguish. We will get through these adolescent years with the minimum of suicide. Two boys at Eton have already left for another world, I have been told: one out of a window and another strung up with his own tie. A boy has recently been assaulted in the squash courts so badly that he may die. As it happens, I was a witness. I was at a window looking down at the squash courts at the time in question and so helped the police later with their enquiries. *No, I am afraid I did not see a strange man. No, I do not recognise any of these faces you are showing me.* In my view it is much more likely the culprit was an older boy but I don't say that.

My questions today are for the authorities who allowed this sort of routine to carry on. Obviously their minds were not on the job during the early to mid 1960s. Either that or they knew well and condoned the behaviour. Did they know there were people being raped continually? Maybe not, because they didn't tell. The culture of the stiff upper lip was much too strong. Nor could I tell on their behalf if they didn't want it. What the authorities saw were the successes and happy faces of boys who were excelling. There were plenty of those to look at. The ones that remained invisible were the silent and tormented souls: often the pretty or the sensitive or the most exotic. Isn't life so often like that?

The group I was concerned with contained the gender-benders who should not been at that school at all. Probably they should have been locked away for their own safety during adolescence like rare birds, where filthy hands could not reach inside their gilded cage. There were probably twenty or thirty of those in a school that size and some happened to be in my house. All I could do when their feathers were plucked was to hold their hands if they wished me to do so.

Perhaps the school Provost can speak for everyone at Eton and represent the views of other boarding schools around Britain. I happened to know the man at the time; he was a cousin.

ONE: What you are saying, Robert, comes as a shock to all of us and would be hard for anyone on our Governing Board to believe. We know the activities that go on in our school pretty well and they are not exactly as you describe, not by a long chalk. Boys do not get sexually assaulted hardly ever or we would soon be closed down. What happens is there is a powerful degree of whispering that gets amplified every time a story goes round about some child. Boys love gossip but it is a malign influence that should be hunted down. Our school dictum is mens sana in corpore sano; in other words, a healthy mind in a healthy body. We are sticking to the belief that we inculcate that here and nothing else. Otherwise how long do you think it would take our parents to pull their children out of school?

TWO: What you need in my view, Robert, and all your gender-bender friends is some good military discipline to chase out the cobwebs. The school here provides an excellent service called the CADET CORPS. I advise you to come back to school and join the corps and go on some forced marches across the countryside. Learn to crawl on your belly through the mud and stick your bayonet up the enemy's arse. That's what your airy-fairy friends and fancy buggarees need to do to refresh their minds. When you have finished that, you can go off and join the real army; fight the fuzzy-wuzzies in Somaliland and show some genuine courage.

Father Perceval listened to chapter two of my story right through to the end. He hiccoughed a couple of times and sighed at other moments. When I finished, there was a long silence during which he stood up and went to the fire.

'Well,' he said. 'I don't know what to say to you, Robert.'

'You don't need to say anything,' I replied. 'I told you the full story, sitting in my room at Eton when you first arrived.'

'Yes, but it's different when you're told like that with the details laid out scene by scene. It's more cold-blooded and frankly hard to digest.'

191

The man was looking in the fire as if he was thinking of throwing himself inside. There was a danger that the edge of the padre's robe might catch fire. I felt a strong temptation to rise and sweep the robe away before that happened. But then I thought, this is a man who has his own dilemmas. Let him struggle with his own fires. Then came the thought that I was betraying my principles by that argument. So I sprang off the armchair to leap to the man's defence, knocking away the nearest log from his cassock perhaps unnecessarily.

Father P sprang back. 'What did you do that for?'

'I thought you were about to set yourself alight,' I said. 'But I don't mind. Go right ahead if you want to burn like a heretic.'

In the Easter holidays, I do something rash that sets my mother's alarm bells ringing. I am rude to her girlfriend. It happens over food as preparation is taken seriously inside the lady's home and we are over there frequently, with my mother often staying the night. Something special has been cooked from Elizabeth David's recipe book and I am called to table sharply, not once but twice. Her friend makes some tart comment about people coming to table when they're called. I get up and walk out after speaking a few foul words about people who are entitled to lecture me and others that are not. I hide a few doors down the leafy street while my mother comes out looking for me. I have been smacked by her heavy hands before and don't wish to repeat the experience. Being fifteen will not necessarily protect me and I refuse to be punished with her girlfriend watching from a window.

When I finally turn up an hour later, my mother has changed mood and is looking a mixture of anguished and guilty. She sits me down at the kitchen table and tells me I need to see a specialist in order to deal with my underlying anger and resentment. I offer to apologize for my words but Mum says it's too late for that. She has already arranged for me to see HER MAN. I stare at her in disbelief.

'YOUR man?'

'Yes, Dr Fordham is excellent and very distinguished. He has lots of credentials to his name and writes whole libraries on analysis.'

I raise my eyebrows.

'Is it right for me to see the same person as you do?'

'Michael is discreet,' my mother assures me. 'He'd never share anything you say with me.'

I could argue that isn't the point, using my own indistinct knowledge of psychotherapy. How will I feel comfortable with a man knowing my mother has been confessing to him herself? But my mother is looking at me in that stricken way of hers and my guilt feelings are rising.

Next day I troop along to Regent's Park and on the way I hear the bark of some wild animal. Could it be the barking of a seal? I ask someone passing by and he says the sound is coming from the zoo round the corner. For some reason that sets me laughing madly. I am thinking what noise I would choose to express my situation: a weird bark is about right. I am still laughing as I walk inside the analyst's hallway and take the lift to the first floor.

A small German lady opens the door. She is like my father's cook – the one whose daughter watched me dangle my parts upside down in a tree. She could be Dr Fordham's wife. I bow to her and she tells me the doctor is waiting for me in the sitting-room. I walk in and a tall thin man rises, grizzle-haired. He shakes my hand and I see he is wearing heavy glasses like my doctor, my housemaster and my friend Thomas. All are scientists by nature: it must be something to do with the kind of vision they have of people. I guess Dr F is going to set himself up as another authority figure. I am determined to resist that. He's not my father (who doesn't even wear glasses) and if he was, I still wouldn't trust the man. Like hell I would. What man can you trust?

'Sit down,' the analyst says, pointing to a high-backed chair opposite his own. The fire is a sham: a fake charcoal burner designed to put me at my ease and encourage me to confess as I grow sleepy. I know that trick. The idea is to make the session pass more smoothly and with fewer words; the analyst has an easier time of it. All he has to do is sit there and say nothing. The victim is lulled into a false sense of security. This is a collaborative process, he thinks – the dumb berk.

'Your mother has asked me to see you,' Dr F says. 'The request is unusual but I'm happy to comply if you are. If it doesn't work or you feel at all uncomfortable, please say so and we'll stop at once. Of course whatever you do say will be confidential unless it concerns a matter of your safety.'

I wave my hand to stop the litany. That way half the session goes and my mother will be paying seventy-five guineas for no result.

'Did Mum tell you what happened yesterday when I upset her friend?' I ask.

The doctor nods.

'She did. I don't particularly want to go into that degree of detail. But she tells me you have general worries. I am interested in hearing what is going on inside your mind.'

I sigh and tap my fingers on the leather armrests. So would I like to know what's going on inside me: it's gone awful quiet in there. I notice there are score marks on the arm-rests as if someone has clutched at the sides of the armchair with their fingernails. I must ask Dr Fordham if he has been applying electrical currents to his clients.

'I have been having some bad dreams about Mum's girlfriend,' I say. 'I guess you know all about her.'

Dr F nods. 'Yes, I do.'

'I hate her, unsurprisingly,' I confess. 'Not all the time, just occasionally, for taking Mum away. I had a dream a few nights ago in which I killed her friend with a machete in the jungle. I sliced off her head and the hair continued to writhe at me like snakes.'

'Like Medusa,' the analyst says.

He pulls an A4 sheet of paper and a pen towards himself and writes down a few words casually. I guess he has written the word 'Medusa' and underlined it several times.

'Interesting,' Dr F says. 'How long have Renee and your mother known each other?'

'Too long,' I say. 'About eight years.'

'Why do you sometimes hate her beyond the reason you just gave?'

I stare back at the analyst. He's already had a perfectly good answer. Does he want me to stand on my head and sing like a sparrow?

'Because she has taken my mother away,' I repeat. 'Sometimes literally. They make endless trips to France and Morocco and other countries while I'm cooped up *in school. Then my mother thinks that bringing back my favourite marzipan will make the relationship all OK.'*

The doctor gave me useful hints while I was there about interrogative style, though we didn't get far towards the subject of my father. I made a mental note of some of those tips to try them out at school. Don't be too anxious to hear answers to your questions. Go slow and let the patient decide on the direction. Don't offer your own opinions unless you have to; let solutions come from the client's mouth.

Well, I have a few questions for you now, old grizzle-haired walnut. How come you broke the first rule of analytical practice and took me as a patient when you already had my mother? Having done so, why didn't you offer to see me when I was eleven and could have used some propping up? Presumably you knew about the abuse.

ONE: I saw you when your mother called because I was worried for her health. Her anxieties had worsened significantly, seeing how much difficulty you were having in adjustment. The business over your language at table sparked a decision to do something. She actually shouted at me down the phone which is why I gave in to her demands. I made a clinical judgement that it was holding up her healing process to say no. I suppose you might conclude that I didn't want her to leave therapy: not after many years together. That does represent a lot of income for any specialist.

197

TWO: I didn't see you aged eleven because I'm not a child analyst. That requires particular training. Nor am I a forensic specialist involved in police work. What you would have told me would have involved reports and meetings with social services and the police, maybe even barristers. I would have been called into court to give evidence and my notes would have been subpoena. I didn't want that sort of fuss and it's not my normal form of practice. It was up to your mother to find someone appropriate for that and she decided not to do so. What was I going to do – go against her wishes? All I could do was support your Mum's decisions.

This evening Father Perceval and I looked over the posters he had brought back from Rome. I complimented him on the photo he had taken of the boys standing with their instruments in a courtyard garden, giving cheesy grins at the camera. 'LE QUATTRE FONTANE!' was the name blazoned beneath the photo. The text said the boys would be performing a collection of Italian, English and French hits at the CASTELLO DI LUMAZZA next Saturday at 7 pm. Tickets would cost just 500 lire on the door. The boys would include songs by CELENTANO and DOMINIQUE, THE SINGING NUN as well as THE BEATLES and ELVIS PRESLEY.

'Why Le Quattro Fontane?' I asked.

'Why not?' The mad monk made his usual expressive gestures. 'It's the name of a famous street in Rome with a famous fountain. The boys are fountains themselves of music and of laughter: each one a bubbly personality.'

'But Le Fontane makes them sound like girls,' I said in disgust.

'Yes, a fountain in Italian is feminine,' argued Father P. 'I grant you that. But that doesn't make the band necessarily feminine.'

'You think not?'

I was thinking of little Ludovico with his drums being very feminine. You could have dressed him in a frock, shoved a guitar in his hands and made him into the singing nun any day of the week.

'OK,' I said wearily. 'I'll go down and spread the posters around town.'

Martin and I are in the train running down to the West Country to see my father. It is the beginning of the summer holidays and we are still fifteen. Martin is a faithful adjutant of my crusade at school. He and Jeremy are helping to push back the tide of sadists, at least as far as they come into our range. We have persuaded the head boy he should think twice about visiting new boys' rooms at midnight. We have done that by finding a girlfriend for him as a pen pal. You remember Alice? I have written and asked her to get involved. The head boy knows nothing about the ruse; he just rushes to his post box in the morning and reels back with excitement on discovering a scented envelope inside. I'm hoping this is going to keep him occupied and intrigued until he's safely out of the school system.

Martin has dressed himself like a Victorian schoolboy going home for the holidays in tweed jacket and tie. His broad face looks back at me with excitement at the thought of stately homes and rabbit shooting with rifles; also fancy dinner parties dressed in black jacket and bow tie.

'There's just one thing you ought to know about my father,' I say cautiously when we are alone in the railway carriage.

'Yes?' Martin has a hopeful expression on his face as if he is waiting to hear that Dad is descended in a direct line from Richard I; in fact he is.

'Dad likes boys our age and younger,' I say calmly. 'In fact, he likes them a lot and often takes them to bed. He may approach you and ask you to do the same.'

'Oh.' Martin looks at me in surprise and dismay.

'If he does and you don't want to go to his room, don't be afraid to tell Dad to get lost. Alternatively if you want to say yes…go ahead and do it. It's no business of mine.'

Martin stares at me round-eyed. Perhaps he is thinking I could have warned him of this possibility before we got on the train.

'I don't care what you do,' I say. 'It's entirely your affair. I just thought I ought to warn you so you know about it in advance.'

If Martin nods a little glumly and gets down stiffly from the train, it's soon forgotten in the rush of Dad's enthusiasm. He has turned up in mustard-coloured trousers and a blue cotton shirt, driving a battered army jeep that has been through several refurbishments. He hugs me warmly and shakes hands vigorously with Martin. He takes the cross country route across the fields as we approach the house. By the time we arrive in front of the imposing Elizabethan mansion, my friend and I are spattered with mud.

'Wow!' Martin says, looking up at the crusted stonework, already falling in love with the whole set-up.

At the end of a week, he is lying on his bed in the room next to mine with his arms behind his head, staring rapturously at the ceiling.

'Do you know?' he says. 'Your father's such a fine man. He has so much sense of fun. He dresses beautifully and always smells of lavender and lemon. He's such a wonderful host and talks so well, with such passion about politics and art and architecture.'

I hold up my hand for him to stop.

'OK,' I say. 'So you've taken a bit of a shine to the man.'

Martin nods.

Dad is so keen on seeing my friend again before the end of the holidays that we make an arrangement to go on a canal trip to France. Two young college friends of Dad's are coming along. He takes out a map and points to a route he has heard about, that starts on the river Yonne and travels down to Auxerre where it picks up the Canal Nivernais.

The days are warm on the canal. In order to keep cool, Martin and I take turns to be dragged through the water behind the narrow boat in a rubber tyre. This is a refreshing exercise and also exhilarating as it is easy to be flipped over and dragged underwater. It is also easy for the water to strip off your bathing costume. Martin is hauled back on board holding what looks like a ripe banana hidden under his hand. It's my Dad who holds out the towel and offers to rub him dry.

There is an odd atmosphere inside the houseboat with five males on board. Perhaps it is the sultry late summer days. Some nights and early mornings I lie

202

inside my narrow cot, listening to the gurgling of the water as the boat rocks gently. I ask if Martin is awake and wants to chat. When he doesn't reply, I glance round to see the bunk is empty. The sheet is thrown back and he is absent.

More questions that need answers. Perhaps I should ask those college boys what they noticed or suspected. Perhaps I should keep my questions strictly for Martin. I can see what he finds irresistible in my Dad. It's those qualities I mentioned earlier: he's enthusiastic, knowledgeable, well-mannered, aristocratic. The style is overwhelming for a boy who is missing his own father. But my curiosity goes further. I have pegged Martin as a straight-forward boy with lusty thoughts about girls. Why accept a distraction like my Dad?

ONE: There's all the dazzle of being fifteen and enjoying the display of power and money, going to fascinating places; meeting interesting people and wearing fine clothes. I feel the world is opening up and promising me a future. This is a first taste: a curious taste but exciting and integral to the whole. I wish to become a gentleman; who doesn't? This is what life should be about: training to take your place in a cultured world. Your Dad is central in that way.

TWO: Hinch makes a perfect substitute for my father. His needs are particular but that makes him all the more exciting. I admire the silky sheets. I enjoy the huge attention. I need the experience of love that he gives me and he's helping to complete my education. It shows how deeply a man like that may care for someone he hardly knows despite being a top dog.

THREE: I love it when people act gently towards me. Do you know how rare a quality that is? Your father is a deeply loving man. There's no coercion. It's as though he's thinking all the time about the person he is with. I may be wrong in that but it's an intoxicating mix. I'll do whatever he wishes. I won't go into details but let's just say that your father and I enjoy our relationship and I don't feel victimized.

'Read me some more,' Father Perceval begged to-night after dinner. 'You didn't carry on last night and I'm missing the story. I've grown addicted and you've only given me two chapters so far.'

I had anticipated he might ask and had set aside chapter three from the manuscript I was keeping hidden, inside a space between the rafters. I read through the chapter about my introduction to prep school and my comments about it afterwards. Father P was busy sipping at the last dregs of Chianti.

'So,' he said when I was finished. 'Some interesting comments. I remember having the much the same feelings up in Northumberland when I was being brought up in an orphanage. My parents died in a car accident. I had other relatives but they didn't offer to take me in. I was left wondering why that was and not knowing the answers. You talk about smoke-filled salons and boudoirs. I wouldn't have known about those but I guess in my case that booze had a lot to do with the decision. My uncles and aunts used to spend their evenings in the local pissoir, by all accounts. It was hardly surprising they didn't want me there where it would spoil their drinking.'

I wasn't sure what to say about that. You mustn't equate one person's suffering with another's. I couldn't exactly say his relatives' indifference was hardly to be compared with my father's white handkerchief.

I came to bed in a strange mood, wondering how this visit to Italy is going to end. Am I going to come home smelling of roses or covered in shit? I decided I would get into bed and focus my mind on hunting for the girl I wanted in the future. I would search the world in the darkness and locate my princess whether she was in Europe, America or the Far East. Then I would fall asleep dreaming of how I would persuade the poor fool to marry me.

*A month into the autumn term, I discover another
new boy crouching in a darkened doorway after lights
out, refusing to go to his room. I haul him into mine to
encourage him to give an account of himself. At first
Charles won't speak and pretends he prefers crouching
in a draughty corridor to any degree of comfort. Finally
he stutters that he is afraid of being attacked if he returns to his room and gets undressed for bed.*

'By whom?' I ask.

*At first he won't tell me: the usual stiff upper lip is
on display. But Charles confesses at last that he is being
terrorized by a group of second year boys. They want to
strip him naked and parade his body round the house to
show off the fact that he's still immature.*

'Why would they want to do that?' I ask, knowing
how gangs need little reason for doing anything of the
sort.

'I pretended in the washroom that I'm fully developed,' Charles sobs like a baby. 'When I'm not at all. I
don't have a single hair on my body. It was silly of me
but I thought I had to pretend to be more grown up.'

I sigh.

'Do you have prep tomorrow?' I ask.

*The school system is based on the idea of boys
working in their rooms to hand in essays for the follow-*

206

ing day. Eton is supposed to operate like a University. Huh! What about safety first?

'Yes, I have tons of homework that I need to do,' the boy moans. 'I'm going to be in deep trouble with the masters.'

'Fine. We'll go together to your room and fetch the homework. You can do your prep sitting at my table and go back to your room later. If Mr Lawrence comes round on one of his tours, I'll ask his blessing to keep you here as long as it takes.'

The boy stares at me white-faced.

'You would do that for me? You won't tell the housemaster about my debagging? Otherwise I'll die. Seriously, I'll curl up and stop my heart, or else throw myself out of a window.'

'No, you won't,' I say, shaking my head. 'Don't be such a silly boy. But I won't say anything if you don't want.'

I debate next day with Jeremy and Martin how we're going to handle this situation. We decide that a debagging cannot be avoided otherwise the threat will hang over Charles for the whole of the next year. What we CAN do is stand over the sadistic gang while they pull off his clothes and make sure the stripping is done reasonably. There's going to be no parading down the corridors or funny jokes about his babyish condition. Martin carries the invitation to the gang at teatime. The boys arrive at six. Charles shivers in the centre of the room waiting for his feathers to be plucked. Martin takes up position by the door like a hefty corporal. Jeremy helps the boy to undress in front of his tormentors, who jeer and try to pinch his white skin. The sobbing *child is left lying on the floor like a calf newly born. The gang of boys files out, looking somewhat ashamed of themselves at last. We help the boy to redress and ten minutes later we are all laughing as if it was all a huge joke. The problem has been resolved.*

A few days later some boys are playing blind man's buff in my room and young Charles is one. He is wearing the scarf tied round his eyes. He stumbles into me and explores my jacket and face with his hands, trying to guess who it is. He recognises me by some detail and lays his head quietly against my chest.

'What's that for?' I ask in a whisper.

'I'm so grateful to you,' he murmurs.

I could easily ask Charles to repay the favour. This is how the school system works. I could have him visit my room at night for the next month if I chose to. He would be glad to play his part like I did as a child. The invitation needs only a word. But that would mean my battle with Dad's demons has been lost. The monsters will have won the war. One victory will lead to the next and my father's ways will live on in me.

Instead I turn away and announce the game is over. I ask Charles to return to his room and avoid looking again at those china blue eyes.

More questions for me this time. Or perhaps I have already answered them. Of more interest perhaps would be a response from Charles. Why did he lay his head against my chest? Was it simple gratitude or a genuine offer? Had he worked out the fact that suitable pay-offs were the way the system worked?

ONE: Obviously I couldn't remain an innocent in a rapacious environment. That's a bit like playing sheep in a den of wolves. It was time to wake up to my position. People were looking at me and making lewd remarks. That's why the second years had picked on me. I had a debt to repay once that was settled. I thought I must adapt: spend time with you, then curry favour with the leader of that gang. After that I might fall under the protection of a member of the Library. Inside a week I turned myself into the New Me. From then on I would be ready to play the game.

Father Perceval was full of excitement when he returned from Rome this evening.

'It's Tuesday tomorrow. We only have a few days left to prepare for the party,' he said, running his hand anxiously through his wisps of hair. 'There are glasses to bring over from the caretaker's house and mattresses for the boys' beds. We need to bring in wine and beer for Saturday and get hold of chairs so people have a place to sit down. Tomorrow I'll take a shopping list to Rome of bits and pieces we can prepare as canapés.'

He was fluttering his hands in the way he did before that Communion service in school. I was telling him to calm down and that it didn't matter: who cared if an impromptu concert was well-attended or a disaster? Anyway, I asked, where's all the money coming from to pay for wine and beer and food? Is the orphanage contributing funds or are they all expected to come from the pocket of my mother?

At that speech the mad monk eyed me with his usual owlish distaste.

'We will have the money from the tickets we are selling at the concert.'

'Which will just about cover the peanuts,' I said.

Father P put on his saintly expression by slightly closing his eyes and acting like Saint Sebastian being pierced by my sarcasm.

'Don't you think that boys like that deserve a decent launch?' he asked as if the request was simple. 'This may be the start of four important new careers. Would you deny them that?'

I groaned and made the sound of a harp playing a heavenly tune.

'Give over,' I said. 'You simply fancy the lead singer. That's all there is to this and don't deny it.'

My father writes to me a few weeks before the end of the autumn half to announce he is going shooting and fishing in Scotland for a few days. Would I like to go with him? The answer is yes, though I am wondering what the bed arrangements are going to be: maybe he has in mind a game of musical mattresses. Surely I am growing a little old for that, having just passed my sixteenth birthday. He must have fresher, younger interests in mind.

When the holidays begin, we travel north in his Bentley and arrive by evening at an old manor house with great lawns sweeping down towards the river Tay. We go fishing next day with rods and waders. I am helped by a bearded ghillie who teaches me how to cast a fly without catching my father with the backward sweep. What a good idea! He points out likely places where the water eddies and creates a hollow. After repeated attempts to land the fly, I am successful. Immediately I catch a salmon so large that it takes me an hour to land the fish. The ghillie dances up and down and orders me to keep my rod high in the air.

'The rod, boy. You're lowering it too much. The salmon will jerk away. Keep it up!'

Lying silvery green on the bank, the salmon measures thirteen and a half pounds on the ghillie's *scales: that's six kilos. The length seems almost to match me. Dad is busy taking photographs. We march back to the manor house in triumph where I am feted by the owners.*

That evening when I am basking in my glory surrounded by Dad's Scottish friends, an old lady walks into the room; she is the grandmother of the clan. Dad orders me to stand and give her my chair. I frown at his insistence. What right does he have to order me about? I am king of the castle right now.

'No,' I say, holding onto my chair.

'I say you will STAND.' My father walks over to me and drags me upright by the arm.

I stare at him in shock and horror. The Scottish family is watching while the old lady is protesting that it's quite all right, she will find another place.

'I don't know how you think you can order me about,' I say indignantly to Dad.

'Because I am your father.'

A long moment passes while I consider my next words. Are you really? I might ask. Don't you think you've rather lost the right to be called that?

As though he can see the degree of revolt that might be about to happen, Dad loses his temper suddenly.

'Go to your room!' he demands. 'And stay there until I come.'

I walk out of the sitting-room, leaving a stunned silence behind me. The giant salmon has turned to dust. The Highland heather has lost all magic. I am wondering what's coming next. Is my Dad expecting to come upstairs and beat me like a little boy? Or perhaps he

will fuck me. Perhaps I should arm myself with the pok-
er from the fire-place and beat him to death when he
comes to the door.

I pull open the drawers of the elegant Louis XVI
desk which is set up to face the river. Inside there are
sheets of headed writing paper lying on a blotter. I bring
them out and find a pen. I write a letter, addressed to the
editor of the Sunday Times.

Dear Sir,
You may be aware that my father is Victor
Montagu, having renounced his title created in
the seventeenth century for restoring the king to
the throne. It may interest you to know that my
father has conducted a sexual relationship with
me since I was seven years old. This developed
into rape by the time I was eleven, at which
time the relationship was discovered by a sister.
Since that time my father has started similar
relationships with other boys. One of them is a
close school friend called Martin but there are
others that I know about.

In my view my father's deeds require a full
investigation by the police and I would be glad if
you started a campaign to achieve that. Certainly
the man has lost the right to be called my father
and should be prosecuted for his crimes.

Yours sincerely,
Robert Montagu.

I stare at the letter, satisfied with all it contains. I
then fold it into an envelope with shaking hands, address
the front to The Editor, Sunday Times, Fleet St, London,

213

and mark it PERSONAL in the left-hand corner. After that I settle down to write an identical letter to the editor of The Sunday Telegraph, The Sunday Express and most of the other weekend and daily national newspapers including the Scottish Herald. When I have finished that, I hold the letters in my hand as if weighing the career of my father in the balance. All the letters need are stamps and the nearest post box to set the denunciation in motion.

I wait until after the dinner hour has gone until I hear the sound of my father's footsteps on the stairs. He knocks and enters without waiting for an invitation. He is carrying a tray of food which he sets down on the desk where I have prepared the letters. I am standing by the window, having thrust them in a drawer. He turns towards me when I say nothing.

'I have brought you some food, Robert.'

I wait. Is he going to apologize or ask me to take off my clothes? His career and future life depends on the next minute.

'I want to say that I'm sorry for my outburst downstairs,' Dad says. 'I was furious with your disrespect towards an old lady. However I went too far in shouting at you. I am sorry for that.'

I turn to him, so choked with emotion that I could burst into tears. Actually no tears are adequate to describe my mixed feelings.

I'm so glad you said that, I'd like to say. You've no idea, Dad, how close you came to disaster.

Well, well. How do I follow that scene with any questions? The narrative speaks for itself. One curiosity is, would I have sent the letters if there had been no apology from him?

ONE: As sure as hell, I would have done! I had been planning to sneak out to the village early to be sure to send the letters off before breakfast. Some instinct of my Dad's must have warned him what was afoot, unless it was an inspiration of the devil. I guess you develop instincts as a politician for back-stabbing. Isn't it curious how a little incident like that can cause such a big reaction? But he headed it off and that was the deal I had made with myself: if Dad apologized, I wouldn't post the letters. You can call that cowardice if you like but there it is.

The caretaker took us this morning to a locked store room in the castle where there were mattresses lined up in cellophane packets. We carried them slipping and sliding up the stairs and dumped them on the iron-framed beds while the signora brought up pillows. She grumbled about the need for sheets but Father Perceval promised to pay for laundry so she went and returned with a bottom sheet and blanket for each bed. The padre then asked for towels and she gave him a severe glance up and down before promising to deliver some tomorrow.

'Supermarket,' Father P muttered before he went off this morning. 'Go round the town and find a suitable place to buy some booze. Make a deal with the manager for sale or return.' He fished inside his pocket and started counting out some notes. 'Here's ten thousand lire. Lay on two dozen bottles of beer and a dozen bottles of wine. Get them to write on the receipt that they'll accept back whatever we don't use.'

I nodded, wishing the padre would leave so I could get on with writing before the chores began. I was starting on the most recent months and looking forward to getting to the present. Perhaps some magic wand would be waved in the air when I did. Jesus would step out of the clouds and make a formal speech of congratulation.

I am sitting in the armchair by Philip's bed, watching the boy as he lies motionless and elegant in his silk pyjamas, wrapped in a kimono dressing gown. The days are moving slowly towards Easter and the boy's mood is still extremely low. I am seriously worried he could kill himself. For that reason I have been keeping the conversation light, focusing on the hot summers in Bermuda where his father has a house. Philip can go swimming with his aqualung a la Jacques Cousteau and spot exotic fishes in the water. The trouble is we've been following this pattern for months now and his mood isn't shifting. I have installed a two way walkie-talkie by the boy's bed so he can call me in the night if he is tempted to go flying like Peter Pan.

'I tell you what,' I say suddenly, deciding to seize the nettle rather than avoid the sting. 'There's nothing we can do about what happened in your first half here. The boys who broke into your room are long since gone on to University. There's no advantage in brooding over what they did to you. But we could set out to catch a smaller fish who added to your woes. Ernie's still with us. We could make him own up to what he did the night before the summer holidays. Wouldn't that help to make you feel better?'

Philip draws in a long breath and looks at me with those languid eyes of his that half the boys at Eton sit up and write poems about at night.

'How do you suppose we're going to get him to confess?' he asks.

I'm thinking quickly. It would have to be a clever trick. Hypnotism won't do at all. The boy would deny everything he said as soon as he was fully conscious. Even a kangaroo court would find evidence obtained through hypnotism questionable. No, what we need is a scheme to get Ernie in my room where he can be interrogated by his peers. It would have to be a voluntary attendance. But how to lure him into such a trap?

'If it could be fixed that Ernie confesses to his assault, would you take part?' I ask. 'Someone else would ask all the questions on your behalf. All you have to do is listen and then accept his humble apology.'

'Who would do the questioning?'

'Probably Jeremy. He makes a good inquisitor and knows what happened.'

Philip makes a curious sound like a whine.

'If Ernie fell at your feet,' I say, 'and begged forgiveness in front of a crowded room, wouldn't that be good for you?'

'Let me think about it,' says Philip. He waves his languid hand and I am dismissed.

I discuss the idea of a kangaroo court with the usual supporters. Jeremy is enthusiastic. He wants to prosecute as he says he knows a good deal about sexual harassment. He tells me I can act as the court president while Martin can be the officer on duty. News comes from Philip that he has fallen for my idea. We work out the best strategy to attract Ernie to my room – ah yes! He comes often when I am giving a hypnosis session. Perhaps he likes to watch that moment when I make people faint. Jeremy will start as the subject and then we'll turn the tables on Ernie halfway through the exercise.

The date for the session arrives on a Wednesday, soon after tea. The performance has been well advertised. A crowd of at least ten assembles in my room. There are people jockeying for a place to sit. I have installed a tape recorder inside my ottoman with the lid ajar so the trial can be recorded. That way if Ernie refuses to prostrate himself, we will have a recording to verify what he has admitted. It can be played back to the housemaster.

Jeremy crouches like a frog in the centre of the room when there is a hush. My fingers start to work on his spinal cord to interrupt the flow of blood. I stop in mid movement and appear to change my mind.

'Perhaps we won't do hypnotism at all today,' I say, returning to my seat. 'Perhaps after all we could talk about an incident that happened here two years ago, at the end of the summer half.'

Jeremy takes over from me, returning to the ottoman where he was perched when we began. I am hoping he is not squashing the lid in such a way that the tape recorder will not pick up the sound.

'Good idea,' he continues. 'This was a serious incident that was never reported to Wettie. One boy who is in this room now went into the bedroom of another who is also here and sexually assaulted him. Everyone had gone home for the holidays except these two who were staying a final night. The victim was asleep in bed at the time.'

As we glance round each other's faces, Ernie is beginning to sweat. An expression of surprise, alarm and embarrassment flits across his face in quick succession. He tries to bolt and Martin performs his officer of the court duty by blocking the door. Ernie is hauled back to his seat while Jeremy continues with his statement.

'I'm so glad you have demonstrated it was you, Ernie. Perhaps you'd like to admit exactly what you did to the person concerned. You proceeded to have sex with him against his will. You did it knowing he had already been attacked and raped as a new boy by older boys. They got him on the floor of his room while he was practising on drums and took their turns with him while holding him down. You did much the same. Then on your return in the autumn you boasted to other boys that you had tasted what his arse was like.'

At the end of this account, Ernie collapses in tears and confesses. He pleads for mercy, thinking we are about to hawl him downstairs to Mr Lawrence. When it is clear that is not the case, he begs Philip to be excused for his horrible acts and the boasting afterwards. He kneels by the boy's feet and looks up at him while he says this. A smile appears for the first time in ages on Philip's face. It is not a smile of vindication but of peacefulness.

So...conclusions! What would the Lord Chancellor be thinking of our abrogation of his system of justice? What would the Provost of Eton be saying? Should I instead have asked Mr Lawrence and the local police to be waiting outside the door? That would have meant applying the full force of the law. The interrogation would have been continued down at the police station or possibly at the HM's office. There would have been no full confession as there was no clear evidence. It was one boy's word against the other as there were no witnesses. Philip would have refused to acknowledge the incident because the last thing he wanted was publicity. It was the threat of that which drove him to think of suicide.

An important point, it seems to me, is that exposure of wickedness should not be about witch hunts. In such cases it should have more to do with helping a victim's recovery. All Philip needed was the recognition of wrong-doing and a simple apology; not a public hanging committee. Ernie was unlikely to do such a thing again. Perhaps in a similar way, what my Mum needed to do for me back when I was eleven was to bring my Dad in front of a similar rough justice. The audience could have been composed of family friends and fellow members of the Commons. I am sure my Dad would have confessed before such an assembly. It's hard to deny your sins in front of friends and family and particularly the victim. What a pity that couldn't have happened. Dad's shame would have been such there might have been a good resolution for him. He might have gone on to be the perfect man.

Father Perceval was going on at me this evening about flowers.

'We need floral decoration,' he said, prancing about the downstairs rooms of the castle: the hallway, the dining room with the gloomy kitchen on one side and the sitting-room beyond. 'When I come home with the boys, I want to see fresh flowers everywhere. Where can we get some?'

'You mean locally, in November?' I asked.

The padre made a face.

'Well, if you can't find any fresh flowers to pick, visit the shop in town and fill the place with what they've got. Lilies, late roses, carnations…that sort of thing.'

His arms made festoons of bouquets which might be hung from the cobwebbed ceilings and the stone arches.

'I'll need money for that,' I said flatly. 'And plenty of it.'

'Money. Always money!' Father P dug into his pocket and produced two thousand lire in various forms. 'There!' he said as he handed over the tattered notes. 'You can also ask the housekeeper for some vases to set beside the beds to make the dormitory look bright.'

I could not resist a sly smile.

'Why, Father – are you planning to spend some time up there over the weekend?'

When it comes to Easter, I spend a long weekend in the Isle of Wight with my eldest sister Sarah. There is a girl around nineteen with her. For once my mother has other plans. She is going with my sister Julia to the south of France to visit an aunt. My sister Kate has gone on holiday with a boyfriend. My brother is away in India. My father's house is available but I am quite happy not to go there. I am looking forward to celebrating my sixteen years in a wholly different way, hopefully well-armed with drink and drugs.

My sister's girlfriend comes from a shelter organization in North London where Sarah has been working as a volunteer. Donna has a heroin habit from being injected during her sleep by an adult boyfriend when she was only a young teenager. He thought he was doing her a favour. My sister has been giving her a home ever since the girl walked into the shelter and she has been steadily weaning Donna off the drug. I have seen the girl before at my sister's house. She is dark-haired, sexy and curvaceous. She slinks about doped up with grass but always smiling, laughing with my sister whom she adores.

We arrive in a battered van from London. There are two daughters as my sister is a lot older than me and has been married and divorced by now. One girl of nine is pretty and tousle-haired, the other aged five is dark with ringlets like a gipsy, uncombed but energetic, always running about. My sister believes I am a hero for surviving school and home life despite my father's lurid attentions. Donna gives me a sexy kiss on the mouth when she meets me, pressing her full breasts against my chest. Is it possible she finds me desirable at sixteen? She must be half blinded by the grass.

'Welcome to the Isle of Wight,' my sister says as we walk in through the doorway. 'We're going to have a party tonight to celebrate your coming of age.'

'Whoopee!' I say, my face lighting up.

'All weekend!' Donna exclaims. 'We'll put up streamers and puff up balloons, won't we, kiddoes?'

There's a chorus from the girls who rush to bring in decorations from the van. Pandemonium reins for the next twenty-four hours with not a sign of discipline or ringing of school bells. My head is dozy with lack of sleep and alcohol, a full belly and a head filled of cotton wool from smoking dope. The girls are running around naked on the lawn. I build a dam on the beach which collapses when they stamp laughing on my defences. On the Saturday evening Donna puts on a slinky record after dinner and draws me into the middle of the sitting room to dance. I am conscious of my sister watching and my Dad invisibly lurking behind a sofa, watching my movements from side to side. I want to stop slinging my hips but Donna refuses. She places a leg between mine as she teaches me the samba and leans back until my mouth nestles between her breasts. She is wearing only a skimpy dress so the cotton barely covers

her tanned skin. I am waiting for the moment when my
father comes between us and commands me jealously to
stop. It doesn't happen.

I don't know what time it is when my sister taps
me on the shoulder and says she's going up to bed. We
decide to go too as it's late. Donna follows as I turn
towards my room. She catches my hand and we walk
together. I hope my sister is not watching us. My room
overlooks the rear courtyard of the house and is the only
one with a clear sound of the sea tumbling on the shore.
It's not a bed designed for two but wide enough. Donna
starts to undress me as if she is unwrapping a ripe fruit,
which surprisingly I turn out to be. She fondles me and
then swings a leg over and settles on my lap. I realise as
I enter her there has been no awkwardness about finding
the right place. That has been one of my fantasies: that
the rear end is much easier to locate than the front. I
try not to think of Dad and only feel her warmth on my
penis as she tugs at it with her body. I let go quite soon
with a flood of fluid. I am so sleepy as I snuggle into the
pillow that I don't even worry about what my sperm
cells may be doing inside of Donna.

Well, well. What to say? Should I feel ashamed of
myself or proud? Naturally enough I feel proud as
hell though a little worried about the sperm cells.
I have proved myself a man. What is more, I have
denied my Dad for once. I have managed to keep
thoughts of him totally at bay during the physical
act. So he's the one to answer my questions today.
What did it feel like, Dad – watching me in your

mind's eye from the window sill? You had wanted me to grow up but perhaps not in quite that way. After all you and Mum had effectively kept me away from girls by sending me to boarding schools. Perhaps you had in mind segregation and single sex routines for all time. Perhaps the next step in your mind was a training establishment for prostitutes.

ONE: You must think me a monster, boy. I'm not that, only a loving man; too loving and insufficiently controlled, perhaps. No, I was delighted by watching you and Donna in action. It made me happy to see you in your natural habitat. Of course I never designed you to become two-faced like me. Why should I want that? I think that sexual orientation is hard to dominate in actual fact. You were leaning towards the norm after teetering on the edge of preferring boys. Well, that's admirable.

TWO: My only worries about Donna would be that you deserved girls of a higher status. Look at your background and pedigree. I am sure your mother would agree. You had not been cautious, which was completely foolish. The girl might easily have become pregnant. Did you want to throw your life away, bringing up babies on State handouts? My boy deserved better than that and I blame myself and your mother for not giving you a better education in that sense. Between us we missed so many of the opportunities. We should have taken you to debutante balls where girls in blue satin dresses so often meet the sons of lords and ladies. Certainly they don't roll around in bed doped up with grass; they salute and curtsey and talk about horses. The sex part happens only once you reach the sanctity of marriage. You should listen to me. I know all about how these things are done.

THREE: OK, if I'm wholly truthful, a part of me was continuing to miss US. I was enjoying a range of consolations but they were not the same as having you. You brought me happiness, dear boy. How can I say more? That aspect of awesome love was largely gone from my life. I watched you and Donna in that small bed of yours with the sea pounding in the distance and I was thinking, *my boy's gone for good and he's not coming back.*

Father Perceval reminded me this evening.

'I hope you're ready. The weekend begins to-morrow. We'll be here by six o'clock. What have you done about the flowers?'

'I'm picking them up from the town shop in the morning,' I said. 'Peonies, lilies, carnations. No roses available. A few wild flowers and grasses are growing on the slopes of the castle. I can collect those on my way back.'

He nodded.

'What about chairs for the concert?'

'They're arriving by truck from the caretaker's supplier after lunch.'

'Glasses and booze?'

'Ditto from the supermarket. The manager's assistant is bringing them over in his car.'

'Amplifier?'

'That's coming on Saturday from the café. They're lending us theirs without any charge as a favour to me.'

The padre looked at me suspiciously. 'Does that mean you've been in and out of there a lot since you got here?'

'Only occasionally to watch the billiards. On Saturday the guys are coming to watch us: the owner, the backroom boys, the old timers that sit outside. The posters got them all excited. They're pissing in their pants.'

The padre nodded again and put his hand on my shoulder. 'Well done, boy. There may still be a place for you in heaven. But just promise me one thing. No sneaking off during the weekend to play with your pen and paper. OK? You know what I mean.'

I expected he might ask and was resigned to two days of literary abstinence. All the same I wasn't sure: I might rebel if I got a strong desire. He could hardly stop me getting up in the middle of the night and reaching into the rafters for my manuscript.

As soon as the summer half begins, I am called down to visit the housemaster's study. I must have done something very wrong before Easter. What? Is it about my kangaroo court? There's going to be an announcement that I'm being reported to the headmaster for a beating. Instead Mr Lawrence introduces a man who is sitting on his couch. His name is Father Perceval. He is wearing the brown robe and white tassels of a Franciscan monk, complete with cowl at the back. He is half a head shorter than I am and stares up at me willingly like an obedient servant, even if he looks like a fringe-haired hermit.

'How do you do, Robert?' he asks enthusiastically, pumping my hand. 'I've heard all about you and your good works from Mr Lawrence. He's been telling me what you've been doing for the well-being of the boys.'

I have not expected this. I have learned to be wary of authority and all adult attempts at being helpful.

'What can I do for you?' I ask carefully.

'Well...' Father P glances at the housemaster and rubs his hands in the classic clergyman's gesture. 'I've been appointed by the school this term – I'm sorry, half – to assist with the pastoral care of boys. It's an experiment to see how well the idea works. I will be spending a little time in each of the houses getting to know people; doing the rounds, so to speak, and discovering who requires an extra degree of attention.'

'They all do,' I say immediately. 'From the youngest to the oldest: especially the ones who have been here for a long time.'

'I'm sure you're right.'

I stare at the monk as at a bird somewhat like a Dodo. It's a pity such birds became extinct sometime in the Middle Ages.

'How long have you got to do this work?' I ask. 'Did you say one half?'

'Well, as I say it's a new experiment. My contract may be extended or it may not. That depends.' The padre glances at Mr Lawrence who raises his eyebrows in a non-committal gesture.

'Ten weeks to get to know ALL the boys in ALL the houses,' I mutter, trying not to snort. 'There's over a thousand boys. That's one house every three days. You'd need twenty appointments in the same evening to get through. Unless you are planning to see people all day.'

I glance at the housemaster and he shakes his head quite definitively.

'Well, I daresay I won't get round ALL the houses and ALL the people,' says Father P cheerfully. 'But I can make a start and that's going to be here.' He glances at me keenly. 'I thought I could come and visit your room this evening if that's OK with you. You could give me some general pointers before I go on.'

'Sure,' I say. 'What time is that?' Getting out my diary like a consultant psychiatrist.

'Shall we make it six?'

'How's half past? I have someone before then.'

The padre glances at the housemaster, who nods tiredly.

'That gives us an hour before supper. That should be enough,' the Franciscan says.

I look at Father P thinking, oh you believe so? Are you planning for us to spend the whole three days together?

At the appointed hour Father Perceval knocks on my door. I invite him in and he sits on my bed that I have just unfolded and lowered to the floor, bouncing on the springs and grinning at the squeaky sound.

'That feels comfy enough,' he says.

I resist the urge to tell him that sometimes it feels like a rack and I am being stretched like a prisoner in a Greek myth.

The padre turns his brown eyes on me. 'Tell me all about you, Robert,' he says. 'And what makes you tick.'

I settle in my armchair.

'You mean me personally?'

'Yes. Tell me about your life. Explain why you have been doing all this good work. What's going on inside? It's an admirable aim but it must cost you on the academic side. Your school work must be suffering.'

So Mr Lawrence has been telling him about that.

'What have you been told?' I ask.

'That your parents divorced early, as far as you were concerned.'

'Oh yes. Long since.'

'And you've been going backwards and forwards between them in the school holidays for years.'

231

'True,' I say.

'That must have been hard on you. Was the split between them amicable? Can you remember it vividly?'

I shake my head. Nice try, padre. The reality is not as easy as a thrown punch between my parents.

'I remember nothing of any arguments,' I say. 'I just remember what it felt like to be growing up in different places: my Mum's girlfriend's flat and my father's bed.'

That visit continues in a way you can expect from the tone I have set: with me revealing myself step by step and Father P tempting me to go a little further. Until we reach the climax where I describe my Dad's heavy breathing behind me.

'WHAT?' Father P says with his eyes popping out of his head.

'Yes! But you have to keep this secret. Otherwise I'm not going to tell you another word. You have to promise you won't tell anyone – least of all Mr Lawrence – or I'll never see you again.'

I'm right in thinking Father Perceval doesn't go anywhere else that evening. In fact he comes back after dinner and we continue. That evening sets off a series of further conversations: for me and for many other people. It becomes amusing in its way. I will dive into my files and while not sharing the full details, I will suggest to Father P that he might like to visit a boy in the passageway below or down at the end of the same corridor. When he gets to know the layout, he will hint to me about a tense situation developing with some kid a few doors down that I might be happy dealing with. Reports will come back from time to time about how the padre is getting on.

232

'He loves rubbing his hands together, doesn't he?'
says Philip. 'Especially when you've just been telling
him something tasty.'

So my questions today are addressed to Father
Perceval and in a way to my housemaster and the
whole school. Were you beginning to take fright
at the back door goings-on? – appointing Father
Perceval was a sign of that. Maybe some brave
souls were beginning to filter back the information
that all was not well in the state of Denmark. I had
complained several times about boys' mistreatment.
There had been suicides and that horrible beating
in the squash courts. I don't know whether boys
may have complained about sexual harassment.
Suddenly along comes the padre with his broad
smiles and rubbing hands. Coincidence, hey? Was
he meant to be the licensed counterpart of myself?
Of course I assumed so though no one admitted it.
I welcomed the Franciscan with open arms. There
were too many cases. I told him my own story in
painstaking detail. When he wanted to place the
sign of the cross on my forehead, I even believed
that it was worth something. Thank God, I thought
– at last someone is here to help me. I'm not doing
this work all alone.

ONE: We (the Provost, speaking) were well
aware of worrying factors in the school during the
early 1960s and were determined to do something to
tackle it. Father Perceval came highly recommended.
He was one of many reforms we undertook in

those years to ensure the best control of morality. You would not have been aware of these changes, Robert, as you left too soon. But we were starting to implement a rolling programme of changes. Already since you've gone there have been more reforms and more are planned. The fagging system will soon be ending and those Boys' Calls that were open to misuse. We are foreseeing that beating between boys will no longer be tolerated. What a pity you didn't stay with us to receive some of the benefits. You would have found your amateurish job soon superseded.

Well, maybe and maybe not.

TWO: I (Father Perceval) would like to reassure you personally about the broad smiles as you call them and the rubbing hands. I know I suffer from some weaknesses. What I did NOT do that summer was to use my sympathy for boys in a pernicious way. I am not vile, nor so poorly controlled as a monk. I might have sat boys on my knees and hugged them through their clothing but I never asked them to undress. Empathy was what I wanted with the boys and the power of the Lord's Prayer. I prayed with boys and we would fall on our knees together before the Lord. No more than that.

Well, maybe and maybe not, again.

The band of orphans showed up with the padre as planned about six o'clock, piled in the back of a taxi from the station. I am writing this by candlelight, after they have now all gone to bed. The instrument cases burst outward as the doors opened and I wondered where there was room to fit all the band. One answer was that little Ludovico had been piled inside the boot along with the luggage. The boy bounced out holding a drum under either arm and raced inside the castle hall like a bullet. The others were making oohing and aahing sounds as they wandered in, as if they had never seen ancient stonework. Father Perceval was paying off the taxi and I was feeling like the ringmaster of a circus trying to introduce an act that was already out of control.

'You can put down your music cases here. Through that way is the dining room and the sitting room where I have just lit a fire. Follow me if you please.'

The old crumbling walls hadn't heard such whooping and shouting echoing round the ceilings since the days of the Renaissance. I was wondering where my mind was at and whether my thoughts would ever come together to finish my writing. Then the mad monk burst in, dragging piles of shopping bags and vegetables and telling me there were tons more outside to bring in. From then on it was pure chaos with the scampering of footsteps on the stairs, the laughter and bellowing and pillow fights and feathers drifting down into the hall. In the midst of all this, dinner had to be prepared and yours truly was kept busy laying tables and fetching drinks like an assistant at a roadside tavern. I had to dig ancient candles out of cupboards because the padre insisted on setting 'the right atmosphere' for supper. The only break came at a moment when the boys were playing cards. I guessed it was strip poker from the dirty giggles coming from the sitting room. I had just passed round beers and was chopping courgettes and carrots into a fine heap of chunks to make a sugo for some pasta. The padre turned to me excitedly and asked if we should ask the boys to sing something from their repertoire. I shook my head, dreading more confusion there.

'What shall we do, then?' he asked. 'Especially after dinner.'

'Go to bed?' I suggested hopefully. 'Each one to his own.'

'No, let's play charades. You think up a book or a film that everyone knows and put on a performance with the boys. I have to guess what book or film it is.'

'No,' I objected, hating the idea of playing ringmaster. 'You direct the boys. You speak better Italian than I do. It would be chaos if I tried. I'll do the guessing.'

'We'll take it in turns, then.'

Father P threw two packets of spaghetti into the steaming water and began to churn them with a wooden spoon while I was throwing the veg into a frying pan with some olive oil.

'I'll only take part for a few minutes,' I was muttering darkly.

The padre stood over me, clutching the wooden spoon in his hand as if he would brain me with it.

'You'll take part as long as I do or I'll expel you from the castle,' he threatened. 'I'm not having you sitting on the side lines watching us like a cold fish. I may as well do everything myself.' The padre elbowed me out of the way so he could add condiments and garlic to the pan. 'Now go into the sitting-room and pretend to be the perfect host. Help them play their poker game and check the boys are not doing something indecent or swinging from the chandeliers.'

This morning Father Perceval was dancing with delight as he waltzed into my room, complete with towel to cover his ample belly.

'I'm so happy,' he crowed. 'So happy.'

I raised my head wearily from the pillow.

'Why's that?'

'We're all here: me, the boys and you. I feel everything has come into place. I'm going to take a shower now to get ready for the day. It might be difficult to have one later. You'd better get dressed and lay the table, start preparing breakfast. The boys all eat like horses.'

He went off singing towards the door of the bathroom, leaving me regretting I had not got in first. Father P would use all the hot water in the rusting cylinder and there wouldn't be more available for hours.

Downstairs I made the tea for breakfast in a black mood and laid on the toast. I knew I wasn't going to be able to write again until the boys were gone and it made me realise how badly I needed the daily exercise. Wasn't that weird? I had come to depend on my regular dose of literary medicine. It was a bit like swallowing a bottle of acid pills but there were moments when it felt like a catharsis: the odd Greek word that therapists adore.

When I had everything ready, I wondered if I should march up the stairs and start turning the boys out of their beds like the boys' maids did at school. *Come on, lazybones.* Actually it was not like that at Eton at all because the maids were trained to treat us like princes. It was all politeness: *Time for breakfast, master Montagu. You wouldn't want to keep your scrambled eggs waiting, would you, dear?* Should I be doing the same for this bunch of orphans, placing a biscuit in each of their mouths? That reminds me of being in bed with Dad and swallowing those sugar lumps of his. There's nothing like something sugary to make a boy perform like a trained seal. I went upstairs and banged on the door of the dormitory to warn the boys I was coming in, in case something unsuitable was happening. Of course they were all fast asleep. Ludovico's lips were puckered as if he had been sucking on his thumb. I didn't stir the boy but fled the room as if my life depended on escape.

Later in the morning after a long breakfast, we took a walk together in the valley on the north side of the castle. To Father Perceval's approving nods, I practised my Italian along the way and listened to various accounts of growing up in southern Italy. They were tales of disaster and parental desertion and violence. My own story seemed not quite so stark. When we got back to the castle, the padre promised me a short break after lunch if I wanted to enjoy a little 'peace and quiet'. After that we'd set out the chairs and glasses and everything while the boys performed a rehearsal.

'A short break! Oh, yes please,' I breathed. 'How long can it be?'

I was thinking of my waiting manuscript and writing something about the day.

'An hour,' the padre said. 'No more. Afterwards the schedule will be busy.'

There's no sense in describing the afternoon, now I am back alone with my guttering candle. I am just going to focus on the evening part. People started to flood in early. It was my job to stand by the door and take their 500 lire, issuing a paper ticket before offering a drink. The boys were passing up and down the hall and reception rooms, serving beer or wine and carrying the trays of canapés. That dealt with food and drink. Niccolo was making polite conversation with the bartender who had brought the amplifier, telling him about his squalid life in Naples. The saxophone player Pietro was twirling the short hairs above his ears in the way my geography master used to twirl mine. I watched to see if he would lift himself up but of course he didn't. The accordion kid Michele I saw had a slight shuffle with one leg that reminded me of my wounded sister Julia. Little Ludovico kept popping up under my nose with a broad grin and offering a cheese biscuit with a slice of mozzarella and an olive stuck on top.

The food and wine was beginning to run dry by the time we started the music. Also there was nothing like enough chairs which meant that townsfolk were plastered five deep along the walls of the hall, close to the platform we had raised in the middle. I caught the eye of the owner of the *mesticheria* who made a sign to me of brushing paint. I pointed to the ceiling and he looked for fresh signs of decoration as the music started. He was puzzled to find only grime and disintegrating plaster above his head. I signalled that I meant upstairs. The music was awful, so loud and echoing in that confined space that it seemed both Elvis Presley and the Beatles and Celentano had combined to croon at the same time. Discordant notes from the accordion and sax and guitar and drums wreaked havoc with my mind. However no one seemed to care less and each number received the same rapturous applause. It seemed LE QUATTRO FONTANE had struck a chord among the locals' hearts, as though the orphan boys had arrived home and been reunited with their families.

When it was all over the people began to depart, which they did with regrets and the donation of presents and firm insistence that we all meet again soon to repeat the concert. Niccolo took out a notepad to jot down people's addresses as I was shovelling townsfolk out of the front door and closing it with a thankful slam.

'Right!' Father P clapped his hands. 'That was fantastic, boys. Well done, everyone! Now we're go-

ing to have a beautiful dinner of roast duck to celebrate. Robert will open up more bottles of beer and
wine. You can all play cards while I run around and
tidy up.'

I glanced at him. He wanted me to play games,
I supposed. His answer was to present the first
glass to me and propose a toast. 'ALLE QUATTRO
FONTANE!' The boys raised a cheer. 'Weren't they
wonderful? Don't you seriously think that Niccolo
deserves to go for singing lessons to a music master?'

I gulped down my answer while the padre was
hugging the lead singer and kissing him on the
neck, which I thought unnecessary. I could see he
was already half sliced and was wondering how far
his misbehaviour would go that night. As the boys
wandered down the hall, singing snatches of their
favourite songs and leaving their instruments litter-
ing the hall, Father P reached for me and squeezed
my hand.

'Aren't you happy?' he breathed into my ear.
'To see them as content as this? After all, that's your
business too, isn't it? To bring comfort to the needy
like I do.'

'Yeah.' I patted the beaming, red-faced man
on the shoulder. 'Sure. It's exactly the life I always
dreamed.'

It is coming up to mid-summer when the school will be taking a week off. Jeremy is rehearsing in his room for a final time before the first performance of As You Like It in the School Hall. My parents as well as his will be attending the opening and I doubt if there will be a dry eye in the house. Jeremy will be speaking the lines of Rosalind and we have gone over the part until he is exhausted and I am word perfect. I could act as a stand-in if my friend gets sick. The trouble is I am no good as an actor; also in no way as pretty or as well-voiced as he is. No one is in love with me whereas Jeremy still has many admirers; not least the Orlando he is playing opposite.

The words in the play I feel are written on my heart. They are those to be found in Act Three, Scene Two. They sum up to my mind the whole relationship between me and my father; my ambiguous role which I had come to criticize more and more in the years since. My sense of partnership might have been mistaken but somehow my guilt had always made it feel it had been that way: a double act between us.

'He was to imagine me his love, his mistress;
And I set him every day to woo me.
At which time would I,
being but a moonish youth,

243

Grieve, be effeminate, changeable,
longing and liking,
Proud, fantastical, apish, shallow, inconstant,
Full of tears, full of smiles;
For every passion something, and for no passion
truly anything,
As boys and women are for the most part
Cattle of this colour –
Would now like him, now loathe him;
Then entertain him, then forswear him,
Now weep for him, then spit at him,
That I drave my suitor from
his mad humour of love
To a living humour of madness.'

That sounds to me like the words of an accomplished teenage hooker. Yet that is what I felt like aged nine and ten, every morning I went to my father's bed: a loving son of the variety that can lead a man into sin, inviting what will happen next; seeking to turn his mad humour of love into a living humour of madness. That is what I feel I did: act as a catalyst of madness.

For the performance of As You Like It, my father and mother are sitting in a middle row of the large hall. I am positioned between them like the strip of bacon in a sandwich. We make an unusual Trinity: father, mother and the go-between. When the scene arrives in which Rosalind is describing how she/he will tease Orlando in the woods and get him to fall in love with her/him, I glance at my father's profile to check his reaction. Does he recognise OUR roles in these words? Is that even dimly in his mind? He is aware of my glance and somehow disturbed by it. He will not turn to meet my gaze. When I glance at my mother, she is breathing heavily. I wonder if she has guessed how I consider we are aligned. She will never agree that I played a part in encouraging Dad – who would?

Later in the play when Rosalind and Orlando exchange a passionate kiss in the last act, I watch my father turn in vexation. Boys are making whooping noises from behind, watching Jeremy perform his female role and relishing it. Dad wants to concentrate on the beauty of the moment. Possibly he has fallen for my dear friend Jeremy like so many others. Are two teenage males kissing creating such excitement in him that he doesn't wish to be disturbed?

At the end of the play, Dad excuses himself to hurry away, pleading some political research. I don't have time to detain him further and ask questions. Were you enjoying that last kiss, Dad? Do you wish you could have done that with me in the old days?

Later on I discuss the scene with Jeremy. I am tensed up in his room, shaking and unwilling to return to my four bedroom walls where I will be alone with my Japanese fishes.

'What is it, Rob?' he asks in concern at my tragic expression.

'Those lines in the play are so RIGHT,' I tell him. 'That scene where Rosalind is enflaming Orlando's passion in the woods describes exactly an abused boy's experience with his Dad. Maybe Shakespeare himself played a role like that and knows what it's like. The boy feels as if he has led the other on, even when the man is so much older and has all the responsibility.'

245

'Yes,' says Jeremy, humouring me though I am not sure he understands exactly what I mean. 'Yes, I see just what you're saying.'

OK – the questions today are for me once again. They lead straight from that assumption of complicity. How is it possible I shared responsibility for my father's acts? What was the mechanism behind that belief? Because it's by understanding the mechanism that you overcome it.

ONE: I lay still and closed my eyes every time. I never moved a muscle except to prevent contact with the lips or my hand being pulled in a certain direction. I think I associated that stillness with compliance. As time went on and the acts grew more extreme, the stillness and silence grew more like a collusive act. I could not avoid responsibility for that. The moment shrieked of fellowship. If I had kept my eyes open all the time, my father would not have dared do what he did. His shame would have flared up in his face. My closed eyes gave him permission to proceed. You can't therefore call all the responsibility his.

TWO: Wasn't there a secret satisfaction behind my quiet façade during the day? I think there was a feeling of *Look at me! Am I not the bee's knees? Look who I have salivating over me in bed.* That feels to me like a second proof of responsibility. Therapists, deal with such ticklish issues when you are struggling to help child patients! Don't hide away from the issues because you're dealing with such gory stuff.

246

Engage and help with the recovery from thoughts like these that will otherwise dog the patient's life.

It's now two o'clock in the morning.

I have to write about something that just happened in the night. It was so shocking for me that I am now downstairs sitting in front of a log fire, huddled in my bedclothes. It is still night but I don't wish to return to bed in case the incident continues to another chapter.

Sometime after midnight there came a rustle at my door and I woke. It felt like a large rat was inching through the darkness towards me. I was not surprised when a movement caught one of the legs of the bed and a violent expletive was let out.

'*Managgia! Merda!*'

'Who's there?' I called.

'*Sono io,*' came a boy's piping voice that I recognised as little Ludovico's.

'What do you want?' I hissed as a dim outline started to climb inside my bed.

'*A stare con te.*'

I could feel the boy's cold feet hunting mine and slithering up the sides of my calves.

'*Perche?*' I asked, trying out my Italian. The boy's arms were now snaking about my waist and I realised he was warm and nude.

'*Perche no?*' he replied without bothering to keep his voice low. '*Mi puoi fare confortevole, vero?*'

By *confortevole*, was he thinking we would have sex? Sure as a rat likes cheese, his right hand was exploring my pyjamas. With his left hand, he was encouraging me to reach towards him. I shrank back.

'*NO!*' I whispered fiercely, pushing his hands away. '*It's not allowed. Verboten! Nada! Forget it!*'

'*Perche?*' he asked again in surprise.

Perhaps Ludovico had never been denied before. He took it for granted that everyone wanted to be *confortevole* with him. He was reminding me of myself at his age: assuming my companion had a right to reach for me. I started pushing Ludovico's lithe body backwards out of bed.

'*Torni a letto SUBITO!*' I ordered him. Then, giving up the pretence of speaking Italian, I shouted in broad English: 'Go back to BED! Don't dream of coming here. You're not invited.'

The boy stumbled away, knocking his toes against the legs of the bed once more and letting out more colourful swear words. His pale outline reached the exit and I could just make out his ghostly form.

'*SEI UN CAZZO!*' he hurled the words at me in a whisper before finding the way out.

At Dad's house during half term Martin and I are back to the dizzy round of dinner parties and bow ties. We take a trip down to the Jurassic coast. Dad's old friend Donald lives there who is my godfather. His son is younger than we are and leads us in a merry dash down the grassy slope towards steps cut into the cliff. There is a shiny motorboat at anchor offshore and we help him drag a rubber dinghy in the water past the rocks and seaweed. The boy insists on managing himself: oars and steering, even how best to climb on board the motorboat. Martin and I grin at each other and surrender all authority. We sit where we are told and watch while the boy guns the engine and skilfully manoeuvers the craft into the shallows to pick up our fathers, who are struggling with picnic hampers and freezer bags full of champagne.

We stop in a bay where we are entirely alone. The craggy outline of the shore could be on the west coast of Scotland. My Dad and Donald have ducked inside the cabin to change into swimming costumes while we are lying on deck sunbathing and watching cormorants skimming across the water. I hear a chortle of content-ment and turn my head to see Dad standing naked in the stern, slapping his chest like a caveman. He steps up on the rear seat and poses his arms in the diving position as my godfather comes on deck. Oh no, he's naked too. I feel my face flush as I look away while Dad dives in. I've seen enough of those flabby genitals. I hear rather than see the commotion as the boys are clapping.

The next evening on returning home, Martin and I have finished our baths and are relaxing before dinner. He is using my brother's room with the four poster bed. I walk through to offer him some cufflinks to go with his shirt. Martin is lying across the silk-embroidered coverlet entirely naked, glancing through an illustrated children's book of The Thousand and One Nights. I stand still. I don't know if it is the surprise of seeing him in that position with his well-sculpted bum and private parts or simply the reminder of the beauty of the male form when it is in good condition. Martin glances up, sees me and smiles.

'Why don't you come and join me?' he asks, holding out a hand and beckoning.

I hold out the cufflinks as I tremble and stammer something vapid and uninteresting.

'Leave those a minute.' Martin beckons with his hand again and rolls on his back so I can see his smooth front side and the long curved organ between his legs, which is half stiff. 'Come over here, Robbie.'

I walk over, limbs shaking on legs that have become wooden stilts. There is no bend in them at the knee. I am wearing only a thin shirt and underpants. Martin lifts a hand and touches the material.

'Why don't you take that off?' he asks with a dreamy smile.

I know the sound of that siren call and cannot think of a good response to avoid it on this occasion. My brain

*has frozen solid and will not help me. However there is
the door to consider, which is standing wide.*

'The door...' I murmur.

'Close it and turn the key.'

*Where have I heard those words before? I do what
I am told and move towards the bed.*

I am going to examine that episode in the same
rigorous way as the rest of my text. What does it
signify? What sense does it make to spend years
evading the follow-on if I go and indulge myself at a
moment's notice? Even with a boy my age. Where's
the fight I have put up so far?

ONE: I (Martin) knew that you were unhappy -
also that I had rather taken your Dad's attention. You
were my closest friend. Why shouldn't we snatch a
moment of comfort together? You knew my inner
thoughts and I knew yours. I had always fancied you
to a small degree and thought there were moments
when you returned the favour. Where was the harm
in that? We were exploring our sexuality. There was
an odd situation in us being there: you might say we
were both consorts of the king. Even more reason
to express sympathy with each other.

TWO: I (Robert) needed to find some physical
outlet for the male-male feelings aroused in me. I
needed to do that with someone safe who would
not be hurt by the experience. Martin was the
perfect candidate. The moment was offered and I
grabbed it – literally, you might say. The encounter
didn't last long; it was clumsy but beautiful in its

own way. It helped me discharge some of the pent-up emotions I had built up in school. I couldn't let myself go there so I did it at home. I can't say I regret that.

Hurrah! The boys are gone and I can get back to my routine. The padre took them home to Rome after lunch instead of waiting for tomorrow. He told me he would stay overnight in the city at the orphanage so I could have the castle to myself for once. I could dance the tango with a pillow if I wished, turn somersaults on the carpet and make myself a home-made pizza. I needed just to bring in a fresh supply of logs from the outhouse before it got dark.

I feigned a headache during the morning and pretended I was contracting a sudden flu. That helped to keep the boys at bay. I was dreading another tap on the door from Ludovico. But nothing like that happened. I hoped the boy was not telling tales about my strange refusal downstairs and spitting in the fireplace. At a certain point the padre brought me a bowl of soup at lunch and announced the change of plan.

I was tempted to ask how HIS night had gone. Had he found companionship to keep him warm? But one glance at Father Perceval's monkish expression was enough to make me wise. If he had enjoyed a vigorous night, then good luck to him. He had earned his spurs with his careful planning.

'I think what we need is a short communion service,' Father Perceval says, coming to visit me one evening towards the end of the summer half. 'There seem to be a lot of unhealthy feelings between boys that could be dissipated with a special Grace. I call it the Kiss of Peace.'

I am not surprised that the padre feels some expiation is needed after hearing so many confessions of desire.

'What form of service is that?' I ask. 'I've never heard of it.'

'The Kiss of Peace focuses on prayers of repentance and acknowledgement,' Father P says happily, toying with his pen. 'I have performed it in other schools and seminaries. It helps to settle excited spirits and unsettled minds.'

'Yes,' I say. But I am busy thinking of the kiss itself. Who exactly will be kissing who?

'The boys will be kissing each other,' says the Franciscan. 'On both cheeks. They will rise to their feet after prayers and communion and kiss each other, saying the words PEACE BE WITH YOU.'

I regard the padre with an expression of concern. Does he know what he is risking? The Rape of the Sabine Women.

'When will this service be?' I ask.

'One evening in the last days of the half.'

'Better make it the very last.' I am pondering the mayhem that could ensue if the senior boys get it in their minds they can let go of all inhibitions. Famous orgies of the past will have nothing on my house at Eton.

The evenings before the Kiss of Peace arrives finds a long queue of boys at my door who have heard about the special service. They are hoping I will intercede to prevent an orgy. Philip warns me that if certain boys attempt to touch him in any way, he will knife them with a blade taken from the table. Jeremy tells me it will upset his apple cart if a certain person heads for someone he loves. I hold out my hands to him like Pontius Pilate. Trust in the monk, I say. He knows what he's doing.

The service is performed before the start of the evening meal. Fifty-five boys are lined up in rows behind their chairs where they will kneel in prayer. Father Perceval intones the introduction. He is standing beside the housemaster in his brown robe and white tassels. I notice he is wearing the usual sandals on his feet whereas Mr Lawrence's shoes are polished like mirrors.

'And after supper, our Lord took the cup and when He had given thanks, He drank it saying, This is my blood which is shed for you…'

I catch Jeremy's eyes and he frowns and shakes his head in a worried gesture. I know he is thinking what a mistake this all is, to whet the boys' appetites. He may be right. But I also detect a curious stillness in the room as the padre leads the service towards the redemptive conclusion. I look towards Philip and wonder how he

254

has resolved his feelings about knifing people. His fine face looks composed just at the moment.

Father P walks along the rows of legs, stepping carefully across each pair. He has administered the bread by passing bowls of wafers down the tables. The wine he wishes to touch to the lips of each boy personally, along with some words of blessing. There is much shifting and glancing between faces as he passes by. A persistent frown on the housemaster's forehead prevents whispering and rude remarks. At last the monk returns to his place and delivers the final words.

'With the Lord's blessing, we will now exchange the Kiss of Peace, saying PEACE BE WITH YOU to our neighbours.'

It is clear that people have rehearsed in which direction they will turn and who will receive the imprint of their lips. Some make a theatrical show of the gesture. One notorious thug turns to his friends on either side and throws out his arms in welcome. I am watching to see what Philip does and whether he snatches a knife off the table. He touches his fingers to his lips and swings them in an arc so they reach far and wide. Then he tucks his head down and charges for the doorway exit. Jeremy gives me a solid squeeze and I feel his soft breasts press against my chest. I find myself planting a kiss on the cheek of a boy in the Library that I detest. People are regarding each other with silly smiles and hunting down those they have missed out when the housemaster announces dinner sternly and asks people to quieten down. The kitchen staff rush in to serve food. Martin waves a hand in a signal that all seems well; there's been no obvious debauchery. He was telling me before how nervous he was. Now the service has happened, everyone seems relaxed and there is a genuine buzz of good humour in the air.

Father Perceval comes to see me later in the evening and asks how I thought the Kiss of Peace went.

'I think it worked OK,' I say. 'There was no obvious rush towards an orgy.'

'And how are you yourself, my dear friend?'

Father P knows too much about me to believe that a simple kiss of peace is going to make a fearsome heap of difference.

'Coping,' I say. 'At least the service stopped me from thinking about you know what for a full hour.'

Priests are keen on the message of forgiveness. To them it sums up, I think, the purpose of faith: to reconcile one person with another and one horrible event with a tranquil life. The trouble is that people don't always want to forgive. Some things happen that are too big for reconciliation. They want vengeance to start with: for God to arrive with a big stick and chastise the sinner mightily. The time for forgiveness comes later. Repentance and explanation must come first, then punishment; forgiveness may or may not follow, hopefully before everyone dies. You don't miss out the first steps and jump to the last like the clergy do too readily. *Let's now give each other the Kiss of Peace and forget everything!* NO! That's NOT how it should work.

My father is one example. Father Perceval might have hoped that when I fell to my knees during the service, my thoughts would turn mushy and I'd be all for forgiving Dad and giving him a free pass to heaven when the time came. Not so fast! Where's the repentance, the explanation and the plea for understanding? ABSENT so far, padre mio. What had happened to the punishment? ABSENT so far, padre mio. The request for mercy is a prerequisite for forgiveness.

ONE: (Dad) Dear boy, may I say a word here about repentance? I have explained already my various points of view. I have no obligation to say more but I would like to add a single point. I have had many affairs during my lifetime: more than you realise. You will not be alone in the God's antechamber waiting for explanations from my side. Do you expect me to line up my various consorts and go down the line whispering I was sorry? Well, that's not going to happen.

TWO: I think myself that forgiveness is for priests. You and I stand above such a ridiculous song and dance. Our ancestors helped to conquer the known world. We are descended from great monarchs of the past. We owe no fealty, even to God; least of all to a Franciscan priest. If a monk orders me to my knees, how should I react, do you think? By tradition I should cut off his head and stick it on the battlements.

I am expecting Father Perceval to come back to the castle this evening and frankly I am rather dreading it. I have enjoyed his time away. What if he accuses me of faking sickness yesterday? If he goes on about unkindness to poor little Ludovico who only wanted to be comforted, I might cut off his balls.

There are only a few days left before I return home to London. I must try to pass them without starting a last minute fight. I don't wish to run away like I did from school. If I did that, how would I feel? Lost in a wilderness, that's what. I might as well take off for pastures new across the other side of the globe. Where could I go? It would be a place where there are no fathers to mistrust; no monks with their rubbing hands, no alluring boys or bristling housemasters; no Mums to enrage with my guilt and her own. It would be a land peopled by beautiful teenage girls who will lead me towards the milk and honey.

Mr Lawrence stops me in the second week of the autumn half as he flits by in the hallway, hair awry and late as always for his maths lesson.

'I'm sorry to tell you, Robert, that Father Perceval won't be with us this half. We'll have to manage without him.'

I am tempted to ask why. Did the authorities think he went too far with his Kiss of Peace service, trying to make boys give up their filthy ways? Or does it come down to hard cash? I guess the school has decided to save the fees. They'd rather have boys tossing themselves out of windows than fork out the dosh. I am particularly worried at the moment about a new boy in another house. His reputation for Godlike beauty has raced round the school within days. The word is that there will be an attempt to jump on him when he's alone in his room on a match day. What am I to do with a situation like that without Father Perceval here? Warn the boy's housemaster? Lawrence will do nothing. I see no other solution though the idea is dangerous.

I approach Mr Fryer in the middle of the street as he is about to step up to the front door of his house.

'Sir,' I say. 'May I have a word with you in private about young Fairweather?'

The man stops. He is short and stout with a bristling moustache.

'What is it, boy?'

'The word is, he's about to be attacked, sir. Three seniors will be visiting his room on a match day around two-thirty, so I'm told.'

Mr Fryer dips his moustache inside his upper lip and bathes it there; a nervous gesture.

'What do you want from me?'

'To defend your pupil, sir. Post some boys round his room on match days.'

Mr Fryer looks at me with contempt.

'You must be crazy. Who are you, anyway?'

'Montagu, sir.'

'From where?'

'PSHL.'

The man nods slowly as he reaches his front door. He murmurs my name again to memorize it and bustles inside the house without saying more.

At tea time I am called down to see my housemaster who is standing quivering with fury beside his desk. Mr Lawrence is not normally an angry man; he is usually quite mild. But now he is visibly upset.

'I've just had a call from Mr Fryer of RDF. He tells me he had a visit from you in the street today warning him about one of his new boys.'

'Yes, sir. I'm afraid it's true. Fairweather is due to be attacked any time soon, so I believe.'

'By whom?'

'I can't say exactly, sir.'

The housemaster stares at me owlishly without his glasses on. I suspect my outline is now definitely blurred.

'I'm fed up with these complaints,' he shouts at me. 'I have warned you before that I will be forced to send you to the headmaster if there are more. Now here's another.'

'Yes, sir.'

'You won't listen, will you, Robert? You persist in your folly and obsessive interest in other people's lives.'

Mr Lawrence stands before me shivering.

'Yes, sir. If you call it that.'

'I do. You will go and see the headmaster right now. I will call and let him know you are on your way. I hope that you are beaten – hard.'

'Yes, sir.'

The HM is a small man with oiled-back strands of hair laid across his scalp in streaks. He grins continually and rubs his hands together. Another palm-scraper! He leads me to his sofa for a chat and leans close as he speaks as if he vastly prefers conversation in a boys' ear to any torture.

'I understand that you have been pestering masters in the street and complaining about the dangers to their new boys,' he says in a wondering voice. 'Tell me more about that, Robert.'

'Yes, sir.' I gulp. Is the man genuinely going to take my problems seriously? Will he set up a commission of enquiry if I explain some of the details? 'In this case the boy is named Fairweather. He has a rapidly growing reputation for beauty. That puts him in a lot of danger, sir, like so many others before him.'

'In danger from what?' the headmaster asks solemnly.

'Sexual assault, sir. It happens all the time at Eton but is hardly ever reported. Because no one wants to own up to such an attack; least of all the victim.'

The headmaster puts his head on one side, still smiling.

'Why not, in your opinion, Robert? You seem to know a lot about this.'

'The shame is huge, sir. They feel themselves dirty and defiled. Everyone will know about it, including their own families.'

I am thinking of my own case. I could be explaining why I kept quiet about it year after year until it was discovered.

'That's why there have been suicides, sir. People can bear the rapes but not the whispering that goes on afterwards.'

'Ah.' The headmaster nods wisely, his eyes bright. 'You think you understand what goes on in such boys' minds.'

I turn red and fluster.

'I do a little, sir.'

'You've experienced such attacks yourself?'

'Not exactly, sir.'

'What do you mean, not exactly? You either have or you haven't.'

I turn even more red.

'No, sir.'

Why am I denying what happened to me? I seem to be no better at declaring the truth than other victims.

262

The headmaster taps the back of my hand gently with his fingers. Then he strokes the skin.

'Come on,' he confides in a conspiratorial voice. 'The truth is that you ENJOY hearing gossip tales about rape and suicidal thinking. You LIKE listening to the woes of boys. It gives you a vicarious thrill. Well, that won't do. It's time to pay for those feelings with some mild correction. Do you understand me?'

'Yes, sir,' I whisper.

'I want you to be a brave boy and move over to that armchair and bend over. You must learn not to ENJOY listening to such stories.'

'Yes, sir.'

The HM helps me to my feet. I am tottering as he leads me to the squat armchair. He motions me to take off my jacket and relieves me of the weight like a valet. He looks down at my school trousers.

'Shall I ask you to remove those?' he asks, half to himself. 'And your underpants as well? I can order that if I wish. I am allowed to do so within the school rules.' He sighs heavily. 'But on this occasion I think I'll spare you that indignity. You haven't been before me in the past. I'll beat you with your trousers on, bent over that armchair.'

'Yes, sir.'

The short man smiles winningly and points to the exact position he wishes me to adopt. When I bend over, he arranges the target so I present the best aim. He'll be running at me from some distance. I hear him retreating and there is a long wait while he prepares himself. I imagine he is choosing between

263

several styles of bamboo and there's no hurry. I can wait; it's better if I wait. He rushes at me at last, breaking into a quick stride across the floor. The sting bites through my backside like hot wire. He steadies himself against me, panting slightly and patting my shoulder before walking back slowly to take the next run.

'That's the first,' the headmaster mutters as he goes. 'You're doing well, Robert, not letting out a sound. Keep it up, boy. Keep it up.'

It's all happening very slowly and you can't help thinking he's extracting the most out of the experience.

No prizes then for guessing who gets the questions today: Mr ACT himself.

I'm going to keep the exchange brief and not waste much time on his answers as I feel I know them well. Did he enjoy beating boys? Did he have sexual thoughts about the people he lashed? Did he actually hold up attempts to clean up the school during the years of harsh discipline?

ONE: Correct. Guilty as charged. I enjoyed beating and always did. My experiences during the war led up to that but I won't go into the lurid details. I have to suffer from those all my life and you have no idea about suffering, dear boy, when it comes to that.

TWO: Correct. Guilty as charged. I often imagined in my head that I was coupling with a victim. I'm sorry about that but there it is. The school could have chosen someone else but how should they know? It's not written on the application form to become HM.

THREE: Actually the charge of holding up attempts to clean up the school is NOT at all correct. Many reforms were started under my personal direction and I believe I do as much as anyone to improve the system.

'What am I going to do with you?' asked Father Perceval.

We were sitting in front of our usual fire, with the attractive wicker flask of Chianti on the table between us.

'What do you mean, do with me?'

'I'll be sending you home this week unreformed and unrepentant, without having spent more than a single day in Rome.'

I shrugged at the padre's baffled expression.

'I've been too busy. I've been working hard.'

'Writing about your home life and school. What's that done for you?'

I shrugged again and the logs crackled in the fire. Actually I felt the writing was doing me a lot of good. Why does anyone do anything? Why did the padre have a strong desire to help boys in trouble?

'I think the writing is showing me that I have to find peace on my own. There's no outside person who can help; it's a process I have to go through myself. Coming to terms with abuse like mine is mainly a lonely path. Writing allows you at least to tell your story and put your own questions and answers to explain what happened.'

Father Perceval looked at me for a long while after I said this. At the same time he was taking small sips from his glass as if it were Cognac.

'You ought to become a monk like me,' he offered brightly.

I laughed.

'That's not the right solution in my case.'

'Then what is?'

'I told you. Finding a wife before I'm twenty.'

'Hah!' Father P. 'You'll be lucky!'

Outside the door of Fairweather's room, I tap gently on the wooden panelling. I can see a few eager faces in the passage outside watching me, wondering what I have come for. The high-pitched voice inside the room calls out, sounding wary.

'Yes. Who is it?'

I walk in.

'Hello, Julian. I'm Monty from PSHL. You don't know me.'

The thirteen-year-old is pulling on his football socks, sitting on his ottoman. There is a house match due this afternoon between his team and another. It is shortly after lunch on one of those days that those nameless seniors have in mind for their raid. My bum is still sore from the headmaster's strokes.

'What can I do for you?' Julian asks.

'Listen,' I say. 'It's more what I can do for YOU. There's going to be a raid on you one afternoon like this. Three older boys are going to walk in here without warning and attack you.'

The boy pulls one sock straight and the other crooked while he stares at my face. He starts to flush and the Brigitte Bardot cheeks light up like Christmas candles.

'Attack me how?' he asks. 'I don't have anything they want.'

'Oh, yes you do.'

'What?'

How can I put this politely?

'A fine arse.'

Fairweather throws me a defiant look.

'I'll fight them off.'

I laugh with a grating sound.

'That's not going to do any good. You'd be better off getting a bunch of guys to sit around and defend you. Do you have any friends with muscles?'

The boy shrugs his shoulders. 'Sure.'

'Get them to come here around this time on match days. Get them to bring some hockey sticks. That should help.'

While Fairweather continues to stare at me open-mouthed, I stand up and go towards the door.

'Sorry to bring you such unhappy news. But it's better to be safe than sorry. I'd stay with you myself to help but...' I hesitate. 'I don't belong in this house.'

On the way back to PSHL, I wonder if my warning has been in vain. I guess Fairweather will ignore my message and do nothing. Meanwhile I've put the first suspicion of hell inside that pretty head. I feel like an undertaker, hammering the first nail in the poor boy's coffin.

Back at the ranch, I pack a bag and sort out the various books on my shelves, pondering which ones I will take with me to London. Jeremy walks in while I am preparing.

'What are you doing?' he asks.

'Packing.'

'Packing for what and why?'

'What does it look like? I'm leaving Eton.'

He walks towards me and grabs my arm, stops me depositing Freud's book on dreams in my bag.

'You can't do that,' Jeremy says in panic.

'Why not?'

'Because what will happen to us?'

I stop and face the boy, then take him in my arms.

'I can't go on here,' I say miserably. 'Trying to defend people and being beaten for my pains. Falling in love and not allowing myself to show my feelings. I don't have the strength to carry on. I need rest and tranquillity, as the poet says.'

Jeremy starts to moan. Gently I detach his arms.

'Look, dear one,' I say. 'You're sixteen now and practically grown up. You're through the worst of it. Soon you'll be in Debate and then the Library and able to beat the shit out of other little boys.'

'Don't be stupid,' Jeremy barks, trying to smile through his tears. 'Then I'd be simply joining the ranks of the enemy.'

I shrug. 'Then you must go on as you are.'

I walk in plain clothes down the high street, clutching my bag as if it's the school holidays. I can send for the rest of my stuff after a few days. If a master or some member of the Library asks where I'm going, I will simply say I am visiting the dentist in London and need a bag to stay overnight. I have permission from my housemaster to do so. If they want to see a note, they can go and ask. It's a ten minute walk to the station. Every step is carrying me closer to freedom and an uncertain future. As I pass the door to Mr Fryer's, I look in the opposite direction. I dread the possibility of passing the man; worse still, in case young Fairweather walks past me in his football shorts on his way to play the Field Game. He will flash me a look as if to say, where are your so-called rapists? Was that merely your idea to come and torment me?

So the questions come back to haunt me in this matter of leaving. Am I simply scared of breaking my unwritten rules? Am I simply conscious of the fact that sooner or later a boy like Julian Fairweather will get so far under my skin that I will join the unholy league of demons like my father? The point of staying alive is to learn from your disasters and avoid repetition. If you're simply going to cave in to your animal instincts, you may as well do yourself in. You are no better than the monkeys.

Father Perceval asked me this evening about my plans for Wednesday.

'Are you returning to London on your own or do you need me to go with you?' he asked gently. 'Only I've been asked to stay on for another month at the orphanage, in the run-up to Christmas. I know you've promised to be home in time for your seventeenth birthday.'

'That's fine. I'll go alone. It's not difficult,' I said. 'All I need do is catch the sleeper train from Rome to

270

Paris and then transfer to another at Calais. I have the ticket and my passport.'

'You're sure you'll be OK?'

Was he thinking some Greek man like Athos might try to run off with me again? I was a bit past my attractive years from that point of view.

'I'll be fine,' I said. 'I look forward to the journey and getting home. Mum and the girls will be getting ready to give me another lecture about my future. No doubt my Dad will want to add to that when he sees me.'

Father P looked at me with a big question mark in his eyes.

'So you'll go and visit him as well?'

'I will. As long as he's not looking for a visit to his house. I don't think I could manage the jade green colours. But I'm happy to go to the RAC Club and get ogled by the old boys. That's par for the course.'

The padre hugged me as he said goodnight.

'Brave boy,' he said. 'You'll turn out all right. You wait and see.'

I am sitting on the rocks by the seaside in the Isle of Wight. It's early October and I'm waiting to be called to a family meeting. The grand hierarchy is there on my mother's side: my sister Kate, my brother, my mother's girlfriend and Doctor Scott. Kate comes to tell me they are ready to begin our meeting. Walking up to the house, I find the group gathered round the long pine table in the dining room facing the sea. There are bottles of white wine standing open to refresh the troops. Each person will have an opinion on the runaway from school and they can't wait to get going.

I have no battle plan and no speeches prepared. All I have been doing is watching the ebb and fall of the tide round the barnacles, the winkles and the jellies that cling steadfastly to the rocks along the shore. I have also noticed the occasional scuttle of a small crab. My diary in the house contains a single plan: to join aunt Betts in the south of France and begin a career as a writer. As I walk back with Kate, I can think of no better career for a survivor than to go on jotting things down.

In the dining room a chair is drawn up for me at the table which places me in the centre of the melee. There is a deep silence as I take my seat. My mother is smoking a series of cigarettes and I see from the ashtray it's the seventh inside an hour. Her girlfriend frowns in a signal she should put it out, which Mum does with an energetic stabbing of her heavy fingers.

'Well,' I say with an attempt at levity. 'This is a jolly scene. It looks like a hanging committee to me.'

'We are waiting to hear what you have to say,' my mother launches in.

I sigh, looking round the group of faces. Whose side are they on, I am wondering: mine or the deep blue sea's?

'Do I have to justify myself for leaving school?' I ask. 'I hated it at Eton. I hate what the school ethos over silence does to people. I felt trapped while I was there. Public schools represent a brutal philosophy of life. Everyone gets brutalized: the successes most of all. The successes learn to become dictators and go on to dominate the world. Rape and pillage; that's the style and purpose of the game. I couldn't take it anymore.'

There is a pregnant pause, then my brother's voice is heard. 'I loved my time at Eton,' he objects. 'I don't agree that everyone gets brutalized. You just fell in with the wrong crowd, Rob. If you go back, you will find it all becomes more fun later on.'

'When you get to rule the roost,' I reply. 'And take down people's trousers. That's what I wanted to avoid by leaving. I'd rather join the down-and-outs in London who are struggling to survive.'

There is a heavy sigh from Scottie.

'There's no coming back from doing that,' he mutters.

'You're only demoralized because you were beaten,' my mother says, trying to convince herself. 'If you'd

273

worked harder during the last year, that wouldn't have happened.'

I look at her, sharpening my axe.

'I was beaten for getting in the way of the sadists,' I answer. 'I was beaten for standing up against rape. Everyone's being molested and the masters simply turn a blind eye.'

'What nonsense! Your beating only happened because you were being lazy and not working. Mr Lawrence told me so himself.'

'You were getting rip-ups from masters,' adds my brother.

'The trouble is,' Kate says, 'trying to sound reasonable. 'You have to take A-levels at some stage, Robert. You won't ever find a job without qualifications.'

'I don't care a hoot,' I answer. 'I'd rather go and sit on a rock by the sea and stare at the Atlantic.'

My mother's girlfriend Renee chips in with a smile and a toss of her beautiful grey hair. 'In October? Rather you than me. I'd freeze with the cold.'

'Do you WANT to grow up cleaning toilets in a public lavatory?' asks my mother, pouring herself another glass of wine.

'No, of course I don't.'

'Then go back to school and ask to be allowed to continue.'

'Beg for mercy from the arch sadist?' I shout at her. 'Who licked his lips as he was beating me?'

'Don't shout at your mother,' growls the doctor.

'The HM is a perfectly fine man,' defends my brother.

I stare at John and don't bother to answer. If he believes that, then he can believe anything.

'At least wait until you have taken A-levels before you run off,' suggests my sister. 'Then all the studying and expense will be worthwhile.'

'I'm not waiting,' I reply, feeling the tears starting to my eyes. 'Can't you see I'm well and truly finished with the whole system? I need my freedom. I need to become a man. I need to find a girlfriend NOW. Do you realise I've never been allowed a normal life?'

The statement agitates my mother to a huge degree and causes her to gasp for breath.

'What do you mean, you've never been allowed a normal life?' she groans.

'Well, I haven't,' I answer. 'Surely I don't have to spell it out.'

Well, who gets the questions today? I guess it's a mixture of everyone – myself, my mother, my brother John and sister Kate. That's a great way to end this book, with all of us arguing backwards and forwards for all time. That's just what life is going to feel like for the next few years until I make my way.

ONE: I (Mum) was in agony at your words. I'd just been thinking you were beginning to be all right at Eton when Peter phoned about the beating and you walked out of school. All my dire predictions for you were coming true. I had allowed that bastard of your father to go free and now I was paying the price. He had undermined you and the cracks were showing up. Next minute we would have a

275

total cave-in. It was all your father's doing but also mine for abandoning you. When I shouted about the public lavatory, I was giving you a vision of what I sometimes saw in nightmares. If I'd known what went on at school, I would have dragged you out for sure and beaten the headmaster black and blue. I'm not a bad mother, Robbie: only one who has raised her children and wants to be allowed to get on with her own life.

TWO: I (John) can honestly say I had a good time at Eton and couldn't see what your trouble was. I always thought you had a tendency to see the drama in things. I guessed your difference of opinion with your housemaster and the HM had to do with that. Eton hates complainers as all schools do.

In case you think so, I hadn't forgotten what happened between you and Dad for a moment. Undoubtedly that affected your time in school. Of course it did. But you know in an awful way that Dad's opinion has been the right one? You have to take the rough with the smooth as you grow up.

THREE: I (Kate) wanted only what was best for you. OK, it's true I blinded myself quite a bit, ever since what happened to you came out. I had hidden away the details in my mind; at least disconnected them from the man I knew and loved. I couldn't bear the idea that Dad had done those things to you since you were seven. I blocked out the images that you described to Mum... and hearing you were unhappy at school, I did the same. I had my academic life which was hectic at the time.

I buried myself in that and also with boyfriends. I ignored the letters you addressed to Mum which she copied to me; they were too full of miseries. I didn't want to know.

On Wednesday morning I walked down the hill with Father Perceval towards the station, knowing I was not coming back to the castle ever again. I had my green kitbag and my manuscript tucked among my dirty clothes. At least I knew I had one solid piece of work to show for my visit to Italy. What I was going to do with it, I hadn't a clue.

When we got to the station in Rome, I kissed the padre goodbye on both cheeks like a true Italian. There was no sense in harbouring any resentment and I didn't. He didn't wish to let me go and we stood there on the concourse like two dummies unwilling to part.

'I'll see you in London,' he said. 'If you want to arrange that. Write to me in Oxford if you do. God speed and don't get lost in some Paris brothel in your hurry to find a girl. Also don't give your mother too hard an account of me.'

He giggled nervously as I opened my mouth to reply.

'I won't tell her anything,' I assured him. 'If that's what's making you nervous. As for the rest of it, there were some good times though I don't count the first night we arrived.'

Father P hunched his shoulders and went on grinning, then turned away and marched across the concourse, shuffling his feet in those mad sandals. He was walking with a penguin slouch and his loose robe flying. I found my train to Paris a couple of hours later and sat back in the carriage to enjoy the ride. I was thinking how I was going to feel typing out these sheets in my room in London: over two hundred pages of them. Was I going to shove the completed work inside a drawer, to be forgotten forever?

A few days after I got home, I went to visit Dad at the RAC club in Pall Mall. Don't bother with swimming trunks, he told me on the telephone. They provide them.

I hate all clubs on principle and as I started down St. James's, I watched the pinstripe brigade diving for their smart front doors, like badgers to their holes. At the RAC in Pall Mall, the hall porter stood behind a tall desk like a high priest at the altar.

'Excuse me, sir,' he said as I walked in. 'May I help you?'

'I've come to see my father,' I said.

'Very good, sir. And his name is…?'

'Victor Montagu.'

The hall porter leaned down from his rostrum like a conductor towards the orchestra.

'Very good, sir. I believe your father is expecting you downstairs at the coffee bar. However I have to advise on a certain matter.'

Was he going to start talking about rules?

'You'll need to wear a tie while you are inside the precincts of the Club.'

A tie, for God's sake! More rules even here. I flushed crimson and nearly walked out. Perhaps I should have done.

'I don't have a tie,' I said crossly.

'Then the Club will happily lend you one.'

The major-domo beckoned with a white-gloved finger and a minion stepped forward from across the marbled hall. It was a scene straight out of *Alice in Wonderland*. I as usual was playing Alice. My father could not have arranged the scene better if he tried. After a minute fumbling in a back room with a horrid choice of patterned ties, I was directed across the hall and down a wide flight of steps. A scene out of a Roman movie met my eyes. Beyond an arched marble arcade with a wrought iron railing, a huge swimming-pool in the imperial style opened out from left to right, running towards both ends behind massive Byzantine pillars. Dozens of old gentlemen were disporting themselves like whales, puffing and blowing and kicking up their heels, blowing fountains of spray over their heads as they made their slow, majestic way through the blue water. A row of these wrinkled sea-lions sat along the bank on the far side, dabbling their toes in the pool; great double chins dangling on their breasts, sagging nipples overflowing their bellies, their stomachs settled like distended balloons between their thighs. I preferred not to think about the rest. As I watched, a hairy old beast lumbered up and I could see a G-string slung between his legs like a private joke or an apology. Was that what I was supposed to wear if I went in? My father must be joking.

At that moment I was hailed from a side table that overlooked the pool. My Dad was sitting there in a typical country tweed suit, with a folded newspaper over one knee: handsome in his late fifties, successful, tycoon-like…and deeply to be questioned.

'Robbie, my dear boy. Over here!'

I felt myself being sized up on the way to his table by several gentlemen, like meat on the way to the butcher's: so much a pound and a discount on a hundredweight. Now *that* in a G-string would be interesting, I could imagine the old boys mumbling to themselves.

My Dad rose to embrace me as I arrived.

'So now you're seventeen, boyzo. Well done indeed! What would you like to drink? An aperitif or a glass of wine?'

So far I hadn't spoken. I had planned to keep the exchange to a minimum; to a question or two, in fact.

'Wine will do fine,' I said to the waiter. 'White, please.'

The man bowed politely in his white coat and moved away.

'Well, now,' began my father, sitting down again and leaning confidentially across the table. 'How was your holiday in Rome?'

'Interesting,' I said. 'Most of the time I found myself sitting in a cold, damp sitting-room looking across a valley and writing a book.'

'Oh, really?' Dad said, his aristocratic features wrinkled with surprise. 'That's an odd way to spend your time. I thought you'd be immersed in museums and antiquity. What was the book about?'

I wanted to say, US. Instead I said, 'About my life so far.'

The eyebrows went up, the political blinkers down.

'That's interesting. I wouldn't have thought you had much to say.'

Oh, don't I, Dad? Come off it! I didn't answer as the waiter had already brought my wine. My ears were burning and my forehead felt extremely hot. How was I going to open a debate with this man who had all the experience of haranguing the opposite benches in the House of Commons? I took a quick sip of wine and looked past my father towards the pool. I watched as the porpoises spluttered and cavorted in the water. There was a steamy atmosphere in the place as though we were sitting at a table in the jungle. Perhaps in some ways we were. A stewed animal smell wafted towards me and offended my nostrils. I rubbed at my collar as my neck was prickly.

'Well, I found enough to say in my writing.'

'Is the work finished?' my father asked. 'Are you going to allow me the pleasure of reading it?'

I glanced at him and away.

'I'm not sure,' I said. 'Maybe some day soon.'

'Do I feature in it?'

'Oh yes,' I said quietly. 'On nearly every page.'

My father stared at me for a long moment and then blinked. He lifted a hand in the air and waved it to catch the waiter's attention. Then he made a big business of clearing his throat while the man came near.

'Perhaps I will join my son and have a glass of wine,' he said without emotion in his voice.

He waited for the man to move away across the hall before he spoke again. I noticed he was rubbing his own neck as I had done, as if he too was becoming hot and bothered.

'Well, that's good,' he said at last. 'It's good news that you're writing at least. I'll wait until you're done.'

I nodded and then stood up, gulping down the rest of my wine. I had no words to continue at that moment. I had no questions to ask.

'Perhaps I will go for that swim,' I suggested. 'I'm feeling rather hot.'

'Yes, do,' Dad agreed. 'You know where the changing rooms are, Robbo. I'll sit here and watch. Go round the pool to the far side and through the canvas curtains. The attendant there will give you something to wear.'

The swimmers' eyes flipped over me incuriously as I approached. One or two slowed in the water to take a longer glance. The octogenarian sea-lions in the shallows lifted their heads as if they were scenting prey. Ducking under the curtain, I came into an empty marble stall. A wooden bench ran along the wall under a rack of clothes' hooks. There was a weighing machine in one corner and clothes hanging up but no one in sight. In the next room I found an attendant in a white coat sorting through a stack of discarded towels. I spoke to him about producing something for me to wear and he looked me up and down professionally.

'A small size, sir,' he suggested gently. 'You'll find a basket in the changing room. I'll fetch a towel.'

I picked out a white slip which might just cover my parts if I didn't sneeze. I stripped off and tied them on as the attendant appeared with a towel. I got ready for my curtain call and ducked out in front of the audience in the pool. I saw my father on the far side, sitting at his table in the alcove. He was sipping a glass of wine and looking red: almost misty-eyed. He waved at me as I came out and I waved back like a small child. I was no one's vision of loveliness anymore – not even his; fish-white and over-tall for my muscular structure. Nevertheless I shouldn't disappoint the sea lions. I walked towards the shallow end where they made room for me to climb down the ladder, watching me with their goggle eyes. I let myself down the steps and began to swim. I waved a final time towards my father so they would be sure to know which one he was: perhaps the biggest predator of them all.

POSTSCRIPT

I was rifling through old manuscripts, having decided to have a clean-up as a first act of goodwill towards the New Year, when I came across this old – frankly my oldest – piece of writing dating from the 1960s. Wait - I make that sound like an accident. What I mean is, I deliberately went looking for the work, thinking it was time it got reviewed. Needless to say, I had never done anything about the stack of pages. The work has lain unmolested in a plastic A4 box file on a dusty shelf for many years: written in black ink on lined writing paper curling at the edges, stained here and there with blotches and the grease of candles. Just looking at it reminded me of those early winter days in the castle outside Rome, staring at damp mediaeval walls and hearing those discordant voices of Lucrezia Borgia and her ilk inside my head.

What to do with it? Would it become the centrepiece of the bonfire in the garden or would it live to fight another day? My father has long since been dead and buried – my mother too with her half-Egyptian girlfriend, buried side by side in France. My brother is alive and going strong with several grandchildren. My sisters likewise except for two that have died from natural causes: the second and the last who discovered my abuse. I'm doing well with the same wonderful wife after more than forty years of marriage – yes, I did marry at twenty! - with four children and nine grandchildren. I'm working successfully as a psychotherapist in private practice following a period of time in the NHS. I have also started a Trust to help local children with their emotional difficulties. What would be the point in dragging out this ancient MS –'this old bone' as a friend once termed the subject – to consider getting it published?

I stared at the pages of 'A Humour of Love' for several days trying to figure out a decision. I thought about my current work which occasionally figures men who have abused children or are coming close to doing so. I thought about the method I go through each time of looking at their fantasies together and fishing out the seeds of what started the obsession. Sometimes they suffered abuse as children themselves and often not. William Shakespeare called passion that is driven to extremes 'a humour of love'. Society condemns sexual acts with children quite rightly and predators often justify their acts as love. But this form of 'love' is that termed by Shakespeare: it is 'a humour of love', an apparent feeling and not the real thing. It deliberately chooses to give up all restraint and that is what makes it actually loveless, simply a manipulation. It is a deliberate flouting of the rules of love that are by nature generous and nurturing. Sexual crimes against children are punishable by law nearly everywhere but they are also treatable crimes. Paedophilia is NOT an incurable illness but one that can be reasoned with and overcome. In my view it must on second conviction be enforced with chemical castration nevertheless.

What I try to do in my work with men who face temptation is to build up their resources of resistance. All human beings have those resources in abundance unless they have become animals. There are mercifully few of those in any society. If I am presented with children who have been affected, I work to reduce their feelings of guilt. I know how intractable these thoughts are. The sense of responsibility in a child can be as hard-wired as the sexual obsession in a man.

For that reason every piece of writing on this subject is invaluable because it gives us knowledge to battle against the twin disease: attraction towards children and the attraction towards accepting responsibility in the child. People sometimes ask me at lunch or dinner whether we are winning the war against paedophilia and my answer to that is no. It only takes one in every ten like my father to extend the problem. The difficulty is that the average predator attacks dozens of children, not just one. The number of victims in my father's case probably numbered twenty; I hope I was the youngest. If I took his case as an average, the number of victims in each generation would increase twofold.

Many victims of my father I have met in later life. A few continued to visit his bed as young adults.

Most of them genuinely loved my father despite his crimes. I protected the man and blamed myself. Also I was silenced by the wishes of the family not to denounce the man. I came close to blowing the whistle on that visit to Scotland as a teenager but I held back. We protect our own – even the predator himself. That is what makes us human. Yet it is vital that we do not protect predators when it is likely they will continue to abuse, as he did. We must not hide from reality or from guilt or from a sense of family shame: we must expose the beast within the barricades even when he is a worthy man.

2014